COMPUTER PROGRAMMING IN 'C'

COMPUTER PROGRAMMING IN 'C'

Edited by
Sudhir Dawra

ANMOL PUBLICATIONS PVT. LTD.
NEW DELHI - 110 002 (INDIA)

ANMOL PUBLICATIONS PVT. LTD.
4374/4B, Ansari Road, Daryaganj
New Delhi - 110 002
Ph.: 23261597, 23278000
Visit us at: www.anmolpublications.com

Computer Programming in 'C'

First Edition, 2003

PRINTED IN INDIA

Published by J.L. Kuma for Anmol Publications Pvt. Ltd., New Delhi - 110 002 and Printed at Mehra Offset Press, Delhi.

Contents

1.	Section I	1–20
2.	Section II	21–57
3.	Section III	58–87
4.	Section IV	88–111
5.	Section V	122–139
6.	Section VI	140–161
7.	Section VII	162–202
8.	Section VIII	203–282
9.	Section IX	283–330
10.	Section X	331–347
11.	Section XI	348–375
12.	Section XII	376–438

Preface

The present volume is a comprehensive work of information for the students, teachers, programmers. This book primarily deals with programming techniques in 'C' language. 'C' is a language in computer world giving solution of all hectic problems.

This book is prepared keeping in mind the needs of 'C' programmers. Various methods, functions, pointers and files in this book are explained through programming techniques. The book throws light from basic programming to higher pointer level programming.

The book is primarily prepared for students pursuing BCA, B.Tech., MCA & M.Tech. I shall be failing in my duty if I don't acknowledge the contribution of my father Sh. J. K. Dawra and my family members. Last but not the least, I am grateful to Anmol Publications Pvt. Ltd. for undertaking publication of this book.

Any suggestions for improvement of the book would be welcome and gratefully acknowledged and made use in a subsequent edition.

—Sudhir Dawra

Section I

Program 1.

```
/*****************************************/
/*************    file1.C   **************/
/*****************************************/

# include<stdio.h>
# include "file2.c"
  int a , b ,c ;
  void main()

    {
     printf("\n** ADDRESS OF a , b and c before
     extern **\n");
     printf(" \n\n Address of a = %x",&a);
     printf(" \n Address of b = %x",&b);
     printf(" \n Address of c = %x",&c);

     printf (" \n\nValue of function function() =
     %d",function()) ;
     printf (" \nValue of function mul() =
     %d",mul()) ;
     printf (" \nValue of function div() =
     %d",div()) ;

     printf("\n\n ** ADDRESS OF a , b and c after
     extern **\n");
     printf(" \n Address of a = %x",&a);
     printf(" \n Address of b = %x",&b);
     printf(" \n Address of c = %x",&c);
    }
```

(Contd.)

```
/* Definition of function function() */
 int function()
{
a = 24 ;
b = a * a ;
return(b);
}
```

Program 2.

```
/*****************************************/
/***********        file2.C     ***********/
/*****************************************/

# include<stdio.h>
   extern  int a , b ,c ;

/* Definition of function mul() */

   int mul()
     {
        a = 40 ;
        b = 30 ;
        c = a + b / 4 ;
        return(c) ;
      }

/* Definition of function div ()  */

   int div()
     {
        c = 73 ;
        b = 24 ;
        a = c / b ;
        return(a) ;
      }
```

Program 3.

```
/*****************************************/
/***********      great.C     ***********/
/*****************************************/
```

(Contd.)

```
/****** Find greatest of 3 numbers *******/
/*****************************************/

# include<stdio.h>

  void main()
      {
    int a, b, c ;

    printf("\n Enter value for a, b, c: ") ;
    scanf("%d %d %d", &a,&b,&c) ;

     if ( a > b )
        if ( a > c )
         printf(" \n a is greatest = %d",a) ;
          if ( a < b )
          if ( b > c )
        printf(" \n b is greatest = %d",b) ;
          if ( a < b )
          if ( c > b )
        printf(" \nc is greatest = %d",c) ;
          if ( a > b )
          if ( b < c )
          if ( a < c )
        printf(" \n c is greatest = %d",c) ;
      }
```

Program 4.

```
/*************************************/
/***********      prog21.c     **********/
/*************************************/

# include<stdio.h>
  void main()
      {
       int x = 20 ;
       float z = 30.5 ;
       float result ;

       result = mul( x , z ) ;  /* passed arg are
     int and float */
```

(Contd.)

```
      printf("returned value by mul() -->
       %d",result) ;
       }

/**********  function scope mul() ***********/

    mul( int a , char b)
     {
      float s ;
      s = x * b ;
      return(s) ;
      }
```

Program 5.

```
/*****************************************/
/***********    prog210.C    *************/
/*****************************************/

# include<stdio.h>

    void main()
     {
      int b;
      int e;
      int result ;
      b = 4;
      e = 3;

      result = pow1( b , e) ;

      printf("\n Result %d ^ %d = %d",b,e,result);
     }

 /* Definition of function  pow1() */

 int pow1( int base, register int exponent)
        {
        register int t ;
        t = 1;
        for( ; exponent ; exponent--)
```

(Contd.)

```
  t *= base ;
 }
 return(t);
 }
```

Program 6.

```
/*****************************************/
/***********    prog211.C   ***************/
/*****************************************/

#include<stdio.h>

void main()
{
    int a, b, c ;
    float a1 , b1 , c1 ;
    printf("\n Demo of the arithmetic Operator'/'
") ;
    printf("\n--------------------------------");
    a = 100 ;
    b = 30 ;
    c = a / b ;

    printf("\n a = %d",a);
    printf("\n b = %d",b);
    printf("\n a/b(int) = %d ",a/b);
    printf("\n a/b (float) = %f ", (float) a/b);
    a1 = 15.5 ;
    b1 = 5.0 ;
    c1 = a1 / b1 ;
    c = a1 / b1 ;

    printf("\n a1 = %f",a1);
    printf("\n b1 = %f",b1);
    printf("\n a1/b1(int) = %d ",c);
    printf("\n a1/b1 (float) = %f ", c1);

    printf("\n Demo of the arithmetic Operator
'+'") ;
    printf("\n-------------------------------- ");
    a = 100 ;
```

(Contd.)

```
b = 30 ;
c = a + b ;

printf("\n a = %d",a);
printf("\n b = %d",b);
printf("\n a+b(int) = %d ",a+b);
printf("\n a+b (float) = %f ", (float) a+b);
a1 = 15.5 ;
b1 = 5.0 ;
c1 = a1 + b1 ;
c = a1 + b1 ;

printf("\n a1 = %f",a1);
printf("\n b1 = %f",b1);
printf("\n a1+b1(int) = %d ",c);
printf("\n a1+b1 (float) = %f ", c1);
printf("\n Demo of the arithmetic Operator '*'") ;
printf("\n-------------------------------");
a = 100 ;
b = 30 ;
c = a * b ;

printf("\n a = %d",a);
printf("\n b = %d",b);
printf("\n a*b(int) = %d ",a*b);
printf("\n a*b (float) = %f ", (float) a*b);
a1 = 15.5 ;
b1 = 5.0 ;
c1 = a1 * b1 ;
c = a1 * b1 ;

printf("\n a1 = %f",a1);
printf("\n b1 = %f",b1);
printf("\n a1*b1(int) = %d ",c);
printf("\n a1*b1 (float) = %f ", c1);
```

Program 7.

```
/*****************************************/
/***********      prog212.C     ***********/
/*****************************************/

# include<stdio.h>

  void main()
  {
    int a , b ,c ;
    a = 10 ;
    b = 20 ;
    c = 30 ;
    if( a < b)
    if( a < c )
    printf("\n a = %d",a);
    printf("\n b = %d",b);
    printf("\n c = %d",c);
    printf("\n a is smaller than c and b ");
  }
```

Program 8.

```
/*****************************************/
/***********    prog213.C    ***************/
/*****************************************/

# include<stdio.h>
void main()
{
    char a, b, c ;
    int i;
    /*  32-bit consideration of compiler */
    /*  Hexadecimal in binary 0000 0000 0000 0000
    0000 0000 0000 0011 */
    a = 0x03 ;
    /* Hexadecimal in binary 0000 0000 0000 0000
    0000 0000 0000 0110 */
    b = 0x06 ;

   printf("\n 32-Bit compiler \n");
```

(Contd.)

```
printf(" ------------------");
printf("\n Value of a = 0x%x",a);
printf("\n Value of b = 0x%x",b);
/* & operator  demo */
printf("\n The value of b&a = 0x%x", b&a);

/* OR | Operation */

printf("\n The value of b|a = 0x%x", b|a);

/***** EX-OR  operator *****/

printf("\n The value of b^a = 0x%x", b^a);

/* 1's complement */

printf("\n 1's complement of a = 0x%x ",~a); /*
print in hex */
printf("\n 1's complement of b = 0x%x ",~b); /*
print in hex */

printf("\n 32-Bit compiler \n");
printf(" --------------------------------");
printf("\n Value of a = 0x%x",a);
printf("\n Value of b = 0x%x",b);
printf("\n Right shift operator '>>' and after
some shift operation \n");
for( i = 0 ; i< 4 ; i++)
{
  printf(" Value of b = 0x%x after  shift = %d
\n ",b>>i , i) ;
}

printf("\n Left shift operator '<<' and after
some shift operation\n");
for( i = 0 ; i< 4 ; i++)
{
  printf(" Value of a = 0x%x after  shift = %d
\n ",a<<i , i) ;
}
```

Program 9.

```
/****************************************/
/***********    prog214.C ***********/
/****************************************/

# include<stdio.h>

  void main()
    {
       int b ;
       int choice ;
       printf("\nInput the choice | ") ;
       scanf("%d",&choice) ;
       b = choice > 10 ? choice * choice : choice-
       10 ;
       printf("\nValue of b = %d",b) ;
     }
```

Program 10.

```
/****************************************/
/**************   prog215.C ***************/
/****************************************/

# include<stdio.h>
  void main()
  {
   char value ;    /* value is char type */
   char ch = 'a' ; /* ch is char type */
   char *address ; /* pointer variable is char
   type */
     /* if we define int *address then it */
     /*  may  work but issue the warning*/
   address = &ch ; /* assign address of ch to
   address variable */
    value = *address ;
    printf(" \nAddress of ch = 0x%x", address) ; /
     * print address of ch */
    printf(" \nValue   of ch = %c", value) ;  /*
   print value of ch */
   }
```

Program 11.

```
/***************************************/
/***********     prog216.C    ***********/
/***************************************/

# include<stdio.h>

/* struct definition */

struct rec        /* Tag name */
{
   char name[40] ;
   int age ;
};

void main()
{
   struct rec record ;
   FILE *fp ;
   int size ;
   fp = fopen ("TEST", "w") ;
   if( fp == NULL )
   {
     printf(" File open error TEST \n") ;
     perror("error") ;
     exit(0) ;
   }

   printf("Name: ");
   gets(record.name) ;
   printf("\nAge: ");
   scanf("\n%d",&record.age) ;
   size = sizeof(record) ;
   fwrite(&record, size, 1, fp);
   printf(" %d",size); /* printf size of record
 */
 }
```

Program 12.

```
/*****************************************/
/***********       prog217.C    ***********/
/*****************************************/

# include<stdio.h>
void main()
{
    int a , b ;
    a = 20 ;
    b = ( a = a + 10 , a / 5) ; /* add 10 to a then
    divide by 5 */
    /* and result assign to b */
    printf("\n Value of a = %d",a ) ;
    printf(" \n Value of b = %d",b ) ;

    b = (  a / 5 , a = a + 10 ) ;  /* divide then
    add 10 to a */
    /* and assign result to b */

    printf(" \n Value of a = %d",a ) ;
    printf(" \n Value of b = %d",b ) ;
}
```

Program 13.

```
/*****************************************/
/***********       prog218.C    ***********/
/*****************************************/

# include<stdio.h>
/* struct definition */
struct rec                                  /* Tag name */
{
    char name[40] ;
    int age ;
    float salary ;
};
struct rec record ;
struct rec *person = &record ;
```

(Contd.)

```
void main()
{
    printf("Name: ");
    gets(record.name);          /* period operator */
    printf("\nAge: ");
    scanf("%d",&record.age);    /* period operator */
    printf("\nSalary: ");
    scanf("%f",&record.salary);
                                /* period operator */
    printf("\n Output ");
    printf("\nName: ") ;
    puts(person->name) ;          /* arrow operator */
    printf("\nAge: %d",person->age) ;
                                  /* arrow operator */
    printf("\nSalary = %f",person->salary) ;
                                  /* arrow operator */
}
```

Program 14.

```
/***************************************/
/***********     prog219.C    ***********/
/***************************************/

# include<stdio.h>
  void main()
    {
       int x = 200 ;
       int y = 34 ;
       printf("\n %f", (float) x/y ) ;
       printf("\n %d", (int) x/y ) ;
    }
```

Program 15.

```
/***************************************/
/***********     prog22.C     ***********/
/***************************************/

# include<stdio.h>  /* header file */

   /* prototype function */
```

(Contd.)

```
int fun( int , int ) ;
void output( void ) ; /* global variables */

int i = 40 ;
int sum ;

void main()
 {
int sum = 700 ; /* sum is local to main
                   function */
printf("SUM = %d ",sum) ;
output ();
}

/* Definition of function output() */

void  output( void )

 {
  int result ;
  printf("\nValue = %d",fun(i,i)) ;
  result  = i * fun( i , i) ;
  printf("\n Value = %d", result ) ;
 }

 /* Definition of function fun() */

 int fun( int a, int b )
 {
  sum = a + b ;
  return( sum) ;
 }
```

Program 16.

```
/****************************************/
/***********      prog23.C     ***********/
/****************************************/

# include<stdio.h>  /* header file */

   /* prototype function */
```

(Contd.)

```
int fun( int , int ) ;
void output( void ) ;

/* global variables */

int i = 40 ;
int sum ;
void main()
  {
    int sum = 700 ; /* sum is local to main
    function */
    printf("SUM = %d ",sum) ;
    output();
  }

/* Definition of function output() */

void  output( void )
  {
    printf("\nValue = %d",fun(i,i)) ;
           /* here give error Lvalue required in
              function output() */
    fun( i , i ) = i * fun( i , i) ;
    printf("\n Value = %d", fun(i , i)  ) ;
  }

  /* Definition of function fun() */

  int fun( int a, int b )
       {
  sum = a + b ;
  return( sum) ;
  }
```

Program 17.

```
/****************************************/
/***********    prog24.C      ***********/
/****************************************/

# include<stdio.h>

 int s ; /* Global variable */
```

(Contd.)

```
void main()
   {
     s = 20 ;
     s = s * s ;
    printf(" \n Value of S = %d", s ) ;
    printf(" \n Value of sum function = %d",
     sum());
   }

 /* Defenition of function sum() */
     int sum()
      {
        float a , b ;
        a = 10.5 ;
        b = 20.6 ;
        s = a * b * mul() ;
        return(s) ;
      }
/* Function mul () */
    int mul()
     {
      s = 100 ;
      s = ( s * s + s )/s ;
      return(s) ;
     }
```

Program 18.

```
/****************************************/
/***********       prog25.C    ***********/
/****************************************/

# include<stdio.h>
# include "prog26.c"
  static int a, b, c; /* static global */
  void show() ; /* prototype function */

  void main()
   {
    printf("\n Square  and  Cube of First Ten
    Numbers ");
    printf("\n--------------------------------") ;
```

(Contd.)

```
for ( a = 1 ; a <= 10 ; a++)
  {
     b = a * a ;
     c = a * a * a ;

     printf(" \n %d %d %d ", b, c,a);
  }
    printf("\n------------------------") ;
     printf(" \n Press a key ");
     getchar();
     show() ;
     printf(" \n Press a key ");
     getchar();
     display(); /* belongs in ch2p6.c */
     printf(" \n Press a key ");
     getchar();
  }

/* Definition of the function show() */
   void show()
     {
       printf("\n Last value of a = %d",a);
       printf("\n Last value of b = %d",b);
       printf("\n Last value of c = %d",c);
     }
```

Program 19.

```
/****************************************/
/***********      prog26.C     ***********/
/****************************************/

   static int a , b, c ;
   void display()
    {
     printf("\n Last value of a--> %d",a);
     printf("\n Last value of b--> %d",b);
     printf("\n Last value of c--> %d",c);
    }
```

Program 20.

```
/*****************************************/
/***********          prog27.C      ***********/
/*****************************************/
/** Future application of static specifier **/
/*****************************************/
# include<stdio.h>
# include<string.h>
# include<stdlib.h>

int input( char *) ; /* prototype */

void main()
 {
   char str[100] ;
   printf("\n Input string: ");
   input(str) ;
   puts(str) ;
 }

 /* Definition of function input() */

 static input( char *ch)
  {
   int i ;
   char c ;
   i = 0 ;
   do
     {
        c = getchar();
        ch[i] = c ;
        i++ ;
     }  while(c != '\n');
   ch[i-1] = '\0' ;
   return ;
  }
```

Program 21.

```
/*****************************************/
/***********          prog28.C      ***********/
/*****************************************/
```

(Contd.)

```
# include<stdio.h>

void arm_strong_number();
                                /* Prototype of function */
   int i;                                      /* Global */
   int store[15];                        /* Global array */
   void main()
     {
      int j;
      printf(" PROCESSING UNDER PROGRESS\n");
      arm_strong_number();
      printf("\n LIST OF ARM STRONG NUMBERS
      BETWEEN 100 AND 999:\n");
      for(j = 0 ; j<i; j++)
        {
           printf("\n  %3d ",store[j]);
        }
     }

/* Function to generate arm number strong number */

   void  arm_strong_number()
     {
      long int arm, number; /* local variable */
      int a,r,m;
      i = 0;
      for(a=1; a<=9; a++)
       {
         for(r=0; r<=9; r++)
           {
             for(m=0; m<=9; m++)
               {
                 number = a * 100 + r * 10 + m;
                 arm = pow1(a,3) + pow1(r,3) +
                 pow1(m,3);
                 printf(" number -> %ld  arm -> %ld
                 \n",number, arm);
             if( number == arm)
               {
                 store[i] = arm;
                 i++;
               }
```

(Contd.)

```
            }
          }
        }
      printf("Last value of number and arm are -> %d
      %d ",number, store[i-1]);
        }

/* Definition of function  pow1() */

int pow1( int base, register int exponent)
  {
    register int t ;
    t = 1;
    for( ; exponent ; exponent--)
      {
        t *= base ;
      }
     return(t);
  }
```

Program 22.

```
/****************************************/
/***********      prog29.C     ***********/
/****************************************/

# include<stdio.h>
void arm_strong_number();
                              /* prototype of function */
   static int i;                       /* static global */
   static int store[15]; /* static global array */
   void main()
    {
     int j;
     printf(" PROCESSING UNDER PROGRESS\n");
     arm_strong_number();
     printf("\n LIST ARM STRONG NUMBER BETWEEN 100
     AND 999:");
       for(j = 0 ; j<i; j++)
         {
           printf("\n  %3d ",store[j]);
         }
    }
```

(Contd.)

```
/* Function to generate arm number strong number */
   void  arm_strong_number()
     {
      static long int arm, number;
                                         /* local variable */
     static int a,r,m;          /* local variable */

     for(a = 1; a <= 9; a++)
     {
     for(r = 0; r <= 9; r++)
     {
     for(m = 0; m <= 9; m++)
     {
        number = a * 100 + r * 10 + m;
        arm = powl(a,3) + powl(r,3) + powl(m,3);
        printf(" number -> %ld. arm -> %ld
        \n",number, arm);
       if( number == arm)
        {
          store[i] = arm;
          i++;
        }
     }
   }
 }
printf("last value of number -> %ld \n",number);
printf("last arm number is -> %ld", store[i-1]);
 }

/* Definition of function  powl() */

int powl( int base, register int exponent)
  {
    register int t ;
    t = 1;
    for( ; exponent ; exponent--)
      {
       t *= base ;
      }
      return(t);
  }
```

Section II

Program 1.

```
/* calc2.c */
/* Four-function calculator */
#include <stdio.h>

void main(void)
{
   float num1=1.0, num2=1.0;
   char op;

   while ( !(num1==0.0 && num2==0.0) )
   {
     printf("\n\nEnter expression having number,
     operator, number\n");
     scanf("%f %c %f", &num1, &op, &num2);
     if ( op == '+')
       printf(" = %f", num1 + num2);
     else if (op == '-')
       printf(" = %f", num1 - num2);
     else if (op == '*')
       printf(" = %f", num1 * num2);
     else if (op == '/')
       printf(" = %f", num1 / num2);
   }

}
```

Program 2.

```
/* calc3.c */
/* Four-function calculator */
#include <stdio.h>

void main(void)
{
    float num1=1.0, num2=1.0;
    char op;

    while ( !(num1==0.0 && num2==0.0) )
    {
      printf("\n\nEnter expression having number,
      operator, number\n");
      scanf("%f %c %f", &num1, &op, &num2);
      switch ( op )
      {
      case '+':
        printf(" = %f", num1 + num2);
        break;
      case '-':
        printf(" = %f", num1 - num2);
        break;
      case '*':
        printf(" = %f", num1 * num2);
        break;
      case '/':
        printf(" = %f", num1 / num2);
        break;
      case '%':
        printf(" = %f", num1 % num2);
        break;
      default:
        printf("Unknown operator");
      }
     }
    }
```

Program 3.

```
/****************************************/
/**********    PRINT_SE.C     **********/
/****************************************/
/******* print service routines ********/
/****************************************/
# include<stdio.h>
# include<bios.h>
# include<conio.h>
# include<dos.h>
# include<process.h>
# include<stdlib.h>

/**      prototype functions **/

  void p_u_l(char* );
  void mode_set_printer(char ch);
  void print_string(char *);
  void print_services_title(char *s );
  void printer(void);
  void menu();

/**      end          **/

  void main()
    {
       int i ;
       char choice ;

       i = 27 ;

  do
    {
  window(1,1,80,25);
  clrscr();
  menu() ;
  textcolor( WHITE | 128 );

  choice = getche();
  choice =  toupper(choice);
  textcolor(WHITE);
```

(Contd.)

```
switch(choice)
  {
   case  'W' :    window(1,1,80,25);
                  clrscr();
                  mode_set_printer(27);
                  mode_set_printer(14);
                  printer() ;
                  mode_set_printer(20);
                  break ;

   case  'C' :    window(1,1,80,25);
                  clrscr();
                  mode_set_printer(i);
                  mode_set_printer(15);
                  printer() ;
                  mode_set_printer(18);
                  break ;

   case  'U' :    window(1,1,80,25);
                  clrscr();
                  mode_set_printer(i);
                  mode_set_printer(45);
                  mode_set_printer(1);
                  printer() ;
                  mode_set_printer(i);
                  mode_set_printer(45);
                  mode_set_printer(0);
                  break ;

   case  'I' :    window(1,1,80,25);
                  clrscr();
                  mode_set_printer(i);
                  mode_set_printer(52);
                  printer() ;
                  mode_set_printer(i);
                  mode_set_printer(53);
                  break ;

   case  'E' :    window(1,1,80,25);
                  clrscr();
                  mode_set_printer(i);
                  mode_set_printer(69);
```

(Contd.)

```
                printer() ;
                mode_set_printer(i);
                mode_set_printer(70);
                break ;

case 'B' :      window(1,1,80,25);
                clrscr();
                mode_set_printer(i);
                mode_set_printer(71);
                printer() ;
                mode_set_printer(i);
                mode_set_printer(72);
                break ;

case 'L' :      window(1,1,80,25);
                clrscr();
                mode_set_printer(i);
                mode_set_printer(77);
                printer() ;
                mode_set_printer(i);
                mode_set_printer(120);
                mode_set_printer(0);
                break ;

case 'P' :      window(1,1,80,25);
                clrscr();
                mode_set_printer(i);
                mode_set_printer(80);
                printer() ;
                mode_set_printer(i);
                mode_set_printer(120);
                mode_set_printer(0);
                break ;

case 'D' :      window(1,1,80,25);
                clrscr();
                mode_set_printer(i);
                mode_set_printer(120);
                mode_set_printer(0);
                printer() ;
                break ;
```

(Contd.)

```
        case  'N' :    window(1,1,80,25);
                       clrscr();
                       mode_set_printer(i);
                       mode_set_printer(120);
                       mode_set_printer(1);
                       printer() ;
                       mode_set_printer(i);
                       mode_set_printer(120);
                       mode_set_printer(0);
                       break ;

        case  'S' :    window(1,1,80,25);
                       clrscr();
                       mode_set_printer(i);
                       mode_set_printer(48);
                       printer() ;
                       mode_set_printer(i);
                       mode_set_printer(50);
                       break ;

          case 'T' :   window(1,1,80,25);
                       clrscr();
                       exit(0);
                       break;
            default :  window(1,1,80,25);
                       gotoxy(21,22);
                       printf("\n Choice is wrong
");
                       break ;
                  }
    window(1,1,80,25);
    gotoxy(21,23);
    printf("Press any key to cont.");
    getch();
    }  while(choice != 'T');
   }

  /************ print service *************/
  /************ menu function *************/
/*******************************************/
/** THIS IS ROUTINE WHICH WILL PRINTS FILES **/
/*******************************************/
```

(Contd.)

```
/************* function printer ***********/

void printer()
   {
         int area;
         char file[13] ;
         int tm, bm, pl;
     char status=' ';
         int row=0,i,top_of_page=1,r;
         int p=1;
         int ch,j;
         int num;
         int blank;
         int b;
         FILE *fs;
         gotoxy(40,10);
         printf("Enter File ->");
         gotoxy(55,10);
         scanf("%s",file);

     fs=fopen(file,"r");
         if(fs==NULL)
                 {
                 gotoxy(50,22);
                 printf("%s",file);
                 gotoxy(30,23);
                 perror("ERROR : ");
                 exit(-1);
                 }

    gotoxy(40,12) ;
    printf("NUMBER OF COPY -->");
    gotoxy(70,12);
    scanf(" %d",&num);

         tm=6;      /* top margin */
         bm=8;      /* bottom margin */
         pl= 72;  /* page length */

 /************ title printing ***************/

 fprintf(stdprn,"%30c",status);
```

(Contd.)

```
 /* set position of print head at 30 column  of
    the paper */

p_u_l(file);      /* print file name from
                     30 column of paper */

/****************   end   ***************/

for(j=0;j<num;j++)
 {
rewind(fs);

while((ch=fgetc(fs)) !=EOF)
 {
  if(top_of_page)
    {
     for ( i=0; i<tm; i++)
      biosprint(0,'\n',0) ;
                          /* putc('\n',stdprn); */
      top_of_page=0;
      }
      biosprint(0,ch,0) ;
                          /* putc(ch,stdprn); */
      if(ch=='\n')
       {
        row++;
       if(row==pl-tm-bm-1)
        {
         for(i=0;i<bm;i++)
          {
           biosprint(0,'\n',0) ;
                          /* putc('\n',stdprn);*/
           }

           fprintf(stdprn,"\n%39d",p);
            p++;
            top_of_page=1;
            row=0;
            }

           }
         }
```

(Contd.)

```
            if(row<(pl-tm-bm))
             {
             blank = pl - tm - row - 1;
             for( b=0; b< blank; b++)
              biosprint(0,'\n',0) ;
                            /* putc('\n',stdprn); */
              fprintf(stdprn,"\n %39d",p);
              top_of_page=1;
              row=0;
             }

          p=1;

        }

   }

    /******** end of function printer  *******/

    /********** print service ************/

void print_services_title(char *s )
    {
     p_u_l(s);
     }

    /********  end of print service  *********/

 /*****  title print on the printer ******/

 void p_u_l(char *s)
  {
  mode_set_printer(27);
        /* print wide characters on printer  */
  mode_set_printer(14);

  print_string(s);
  mode_set_printer(20);
        /*Recap the previous mode of printer */
 }

/**** end of the print title service ****/
```

(Contd.)

```
  /****** print string function *******/

 void print_string(char *s)
     {
     while(*s)
      {
      mode_set_printer(*s);
      s++ ;
      }
     }

/******* end of print string function ********/

/********  mode setting of the printer *******/

 void mode_set_printer(char ch)
     {
      int status ;

     status = biosprint(2,ch,0);
      /* according requirement set 2 to 0 or 1 */

          if(status & 0x01 )
            printf("\ndevice time out ");

            if( status & 0x08)
             printf("\n I/O error ");

          if(status & 0x10 )
        printf(" \ndevice selected  ");

      if( status & 0x20)
     printf("\n out off paper  ");

          if(status & 0x40 )
            printf(" \nacknowledge   ");

                if( status & 0x80)
                  printf("\n not busy   ");
      }

 /******  end of mode setting function *******/
/*************  menu function ****************/
```

(Contd.)

```
# include<stdio.h>
# include<conio.h>

  int left ;
  int top ;
  int right ;
  int bottom ;

  int color  = WHITE ;

     void box_draw( int , int , int , int , int ) ;
                                       /* prototype */

     void menu()
         {
           clrscr();

           left   = 5 ;
           top    = 2;
           right  = 55 ;
           bottom = 20 ;


        box_draw(left,top,right,bottom,RED);

         }

   /******* function definition ********/

void box_draw(int left, int top, int right, int
bottom ,int color )
         {
           int i ;
           int width ;
           int hight;
           char *string[] ={
            "Select print Services From The List",
            "W <- WIDE    ",
            "C <- CONDENSED ",
            "U <- UNDERLINE ",
            "I <- ITALICS  ",
                "E <- EMPHESIZED ",
```

(Contd.)

```
        "B <- BOLD ",
        "L <- ELITE ",
        "P <- PICA ",
        "D <- DEFAULT",
        "N <- NEAR LETTER",
        "S <- SPACING 1/8 DEFAULT IS 1/6",
        "T <- EXIT",
        "Enter The Choice -->"
    } ;

     width = right - left + 1 ;
     hight = bottom - top + 1 ;
    window(left, top, right, bottom+1);
    textcolor(color);
    for( i = 1 ; i <= width ; i++)
      {
     gotoxy(i,1);
     putchar(205);
     gotoxy(i,hight);
     putchar(205);
      }

    for( i = 1 ; i <= hight ; i++)
      {
     gotoxy(1,i);
     putchar(186);
     gotoxy(width,i);
     putchar(186);
      }
     gotoxy(1,1);
     putchar(201);
     gotoxy(width,1);
     putchar(187);
     gotoxy(1,hight);
     putchar(200);
     gotoxy(width,hight);
     putchar(188);
window(left+2, top+1, right-2, bottom-3);
window(left, top, right, bottom+1);

    for( i = 0 ; i <= 13 ; i++)
       {
```

(Contd.)

```
        gotoxy(i+3,i+2);
        cprintf("%s",string[i]);
        }

    gotoxy(10,hight-1);
     textcolor(RED | 128 );
     }
```

Program 4.

```
/**************************************************/
/******************* prog31.c *****************/
/**************************************************/
/***   find summation of even and odd numbers   ***/
/************** between 0 and 100   **************/
/**************************************************/
# include<stdio.h>

void main()
{
   int even , i ;
   int odd ;
   int choice ;

   /* Initialisation section */

   even = 0 ;
   odd  = 0 ;

   /***************  end  ***************/

   printf("\nEnter choice  '0' for even and odd
   both: ") ;
   scanf("%d", &choice ) ;

   /* Summation of even number section */

   if ( choice == 0 )
   {
   for( i = 0 ; i <= 100 ; i += 2)
```

(Contd.)

```
    {
      even += i ;
    }
    printf("\n Summation of even number between 0
    and 100 = %d",even);
    }

    /****************  end  ***************/

    /*  Summation of odd number section */

    for( i = 1 ; i <= 100 ; i += 2 )
    {
      odd += i ;
    }
    printf("\n Summation of odd number between 0
    and 100 = %d",odd);

    /****************  end  ***************/

}
```

Program 5.

```
/*****************************************/
/************      prog310.c    ***********/
/*****************************************/

# include<stdio.h>
void main()
{
    int i ;
    i = 0 ; /* Initialisation outside the loop */
    for ( ; i < 10 ; i++ )
    {
      printf("\n Hello Loop Check  %d time", i+1 );

    }
    printf("\n Thanking You ");
}
```

Program 6.

```
/*****************************************/
/**************   prog311.c   *************/
/*****************************************/

# include<stdio.h>

void main()
{
    int j ;

    for (j = 40 ; j <= 50 ; j++ )
      printf("\n Square %d of %d ", j*j, j );

    printf("\n Thanking You ");
}
void main()
{
    int i ,j;
    i = 20 ;

    for (j = 20 ; j != i ; j++ )
    {
      printf("\n Value of j = %d ", j );

    }
    printf("\n Thanking You ");
}
```

Program 7.

```
/*****************************************/
/***************   prog312.c   ************/
/*****************************************/

# include<stdio.h>
double pow1(int, register int);
  void main()
     {
    int i ;
    double result ;
```

(Contd.)

```
    for (i = 10 ; i ; i -= 2 )
      {
      result = pow1(i, i);
      printf("\n Value of i^i = %15.2f  of %d ",
      result,i );

        }
       printf("\n Thanking You ");
    }

/* Definition of function  pow1() */

double pow1( int base, register int exponent)
       {
       register int t ;
    t = 1;
    for( ; exponent ; exponent--)
    {
    t *= base ;
    }
       return(t);
       }
```

Program 8.

```
/*******************************************/
/***********     prog313.c     ************/
/*******************************************/

# include<stdio.h>
void main()
{
    int i ,j;
    i = 20 ;

    for (j = 20 ; j != i ; j++ )
    {
      printf("\n Value of j = %d ", j );

    }
      printf("\n Thanking You ");
}
```

Program 9.

```
/*****************************************/
/***********       ch3p14.c      *********/
/*****************************************/

# include<stdio.h>
# include<conio.h>
# include<string.h>
# include<process.h>
# include"print_se.c"

 char *s;
void password( char *);
  void main()
     {

     password( s) ;
     puts(s);
     getch();
     }
     void password( char *pass)
         {
         char str[9] ;
         char str1[9];
         int i ;
         FILE *fp ;

      fp = fopen("passwd.pas","r");
             if( fp == NULL)
               {
                printf("\n File PASSWD.PAS");
                perror("\n ERROR");
                exit(1) ;
               }
               /*
               for( i = 0 ;i < 4 ; i++ )
               {
              printf("\n Enter Password :");
              scanf("%s",str1);
         fprintf(fp,"%s\n",str1);
               }
```

(Contd.)

```
              fclose(fp);
              exit(1);
              */
                 printf("\n Enter Password :");
                  scanf("%s",str1);
       fscanf(fp,"%s",str);
       for(i = 0 ; i< 4 && strcmpi(str,str1); i++)
              {
              fscanf(fp,"%s",str);

              }
           if((strcmpi(str,str1))==0)
              {
            printf("\n %s",str);
            printf("\n Your Account exist on this
            machine");
              getch();
              print_services();
               }
     if(( i == 4 ) || (!feof(fp) ))
             {
     printf("\n LOGIN TIME OVER WAIT FOR LOGIN :");
              printf("\n Retry ");
              exit(1) ;
               }
              fclose(fp);

          pass = str ;
       }
```

Program 10.

```
/*******************************************/
/************    prog315.c    **************/
/*******************************************/
# include<stdio.h>

void main()
{
    for ( ; ; )
      printf(" INFINITE");
}
```

Program 11.

```
/******************************************/
/***************    prog316.c  *************/
/******************************************/

# include<stdio.h>
void trial() ;  /* Prototype */

void main()
   {
   trial() ;
   }

/* Definition of function trial() */

void trial()
{
    char choice ;
    choice = '\0' ;
    while ( choice != 'z' )
    {
    printf("\n Enter choice (z) to break: ");
    choice = getchar();
    printf("\n Your entered choice is %c", choice);
    }
}
```

Program 12.

```
/******************************************/
/***************    prog317.c  *************/
/******************************************/

# include<stdio.h>

void string() ;  /* Prototype */

void main()
{
    char str[128] ;
    printf("\n Input string: ");
```

(Contd.)

```
    string(str) ;
    puts(str) ;
}

/* Definition of function trial() */

void string(char *s)
{
    int i ;
    char ch ;
    i = 0 ;
    ch = getchar () ;
    while( ch != '\n')
    {
      s[i] = ch ;
      i++ ;
      ch = getchar() ;
    }
    s[i] = '\0' ;
}
```

Program 13.

```
/*******************************************/
/**************   prog318.c   *************/
/*******************************************/

/* Multiple condition checking */

# include<stdio.h>

  void load() ; /* Prototype */
  void main()

        {
    load() ;
        }

       /* Definftion of function load() */

       void load()
     {
```

(Contd.)

```
   int condition ;
   condition = 1 ; /* +ve value means condition
                        is true */

   while(condition)
    {
     condition = function1() ;
                     /* Returned  value of function
                          assigned to condition */
     if (condition)
        condition = function2() ;
                     /* Returned  value of function
                          assigned to condition */

     if (condition)
        condition = function3() ;
                     /* Returned  value of function
                          assigned to condition */

     if (condition)
        condition = function4() ;
                     /* Returned  value of function
                          assigned to condition */
    }
 }

/* Definition of function1() */

  int function1()
   {
     int cond1 ;
     cond1 = 12 ;      /* true */
    return(cond1);
   }

/* Definition of function2() */

  int function2()
   {
     int cond1 ;
     cond1 = 24 ;      /* true */
    return(cond1);
```

(Contd.)

```
    }
/* Definition of function3() */

    int function3()
     {
       int cond1 ;
       cond1 = 36 ;    /* true */
      return(cond1);
     }

/* Definition of function4() */

    int function4()
     {
       int cond1 ;
       cond1 = 0 ;  /* false */
      return(cond1);
     }
```

Program 14.

```
/*******************************************/
/**************  prog319.c  ***************/
/*******************************************/

# include<stdio.h>

char menu();
void main()
{
    system("clear");
    display_menu() ;
}

/* Definition of display_menu() */
display_menu()
{
    char choice ;
    do
    {
      choice = menu();
      switch(choice)
```

(Contd.)

```
{
case 'D' :
  system("l");
  printf("\n Press a key");
  getchar();
  getchar();
  system("clear");
  break ;

case 'C' :
  system("copy prog319.c file2");
  printf("\n Press a key");
  getchar();
  getchar();
  system("clear");
  break ;

case 'S' :
  system("grep pow *");
  printf("\n Press a key");
  getchar();
  getchar();
  system("clear");
  break ;

case 'T' :
  system("cat prog319.c");
  printf("\n Press a key");
  getchar();
  getchar();
  system("clear");
  break ;

default :
  printf("\n Press a key");
  getchar();
  getchar();
  system("clear");
  break;
 }
}while (choice != 'B');
}
```

(Contd.)

```
char menu()
{
    char choice;
    printf("\n D-->DIR");
    printf("\n C-->COPY");
    printf("\n S-->SEARCH");
    printf("\n T-->TYPE");
    printf("\n B-->BREAK");
    printf("\nEnter Choice: ");
    choice = getchar() ;
    return (choice);
}
```

Program 15.

```
/*******************************************/
/***************   prog32.c   **************/
/*******************************************/
/* Find summation even and odd numbers between 0
and 100 */

# include<stdio.h>
# include<ctype.h>
# include<stdlib.h>
void main()
{
    int even , i ;
    int odd ;
    char choice ;

    /* Initialisation section */

    even = 0 ;
    odd  = 0 ;

    /*************** end *****************/

    printf("\n Enter choice O = odd , E = even: ");
    choice = getchar() ;
    choice = toupper(choice) ;
                           /* change in upper case */
```

(Contd.)

```
/* This section find Summation of even number */

    if ( choice == 'E' )
    {
    for( i = 0 ; i <= 100 ; i += 2 )
    {
      even += i ;
    }
    printf("\n Summation of even number between 0
    and 100 = %d",even);
    }
    /**************** end ****************/

/* This section find summation of odd numbers */

    else
    if ( choice == 'O' )
    {
      for( i = 1 ; i <= 100 ; i += 2 )
      {
        odd += i ;
      }
      printf("\n Summation of odd number between 0
      and 100 = %d",odd);
      }
    /**************** end ****************/

      else
      {
        printf("\n Wrong Choice ") ;
        exit(0) ;   /* Transfer control to promt */
      }
}
```

Program 16.

```
/****************************************/
/************** prog320.c **************/
/****************************************/

# include<stdio.h>
char array[] = {
```

(Contd.)

```
        'a','b','c','d','e','f','g','h','i',
        'j','k','l','m','n','o','p','q','r',
        's','t','u','v','w','x','y','z'};
void main()
{
    int i ;
    for ( i = 0 ; i < 26 ; i++ )
    {
      printf("\nInformation = %c", array[i] ) ;
      printf(" and postion value = %d",i) ;
      if(array[i] == 'l')
      {
        printf("\n Search is successful");
        printf("\nInformation = %c", array[i] ) ;
        printf(" and postion value = %d",i+1) ;
        break ;
      }
    }
}
```

Program 17.

```
/*******************************************/
/**************   prog321.c   **************/
/*******************************************/

# include<stdio.h>

void main()
{
    int i ;
    int label ;

    for( i = 0 ; i < 10 ; i++ )
    {
      label = 0 ;
      for ( ; ; )
      {
        printf(" \n label = %d",label) ;
        label ++;
        if( label == 50)
          break ;
```

(Contd.)

```
        }
      }
  }
```

Program 18.

```
/*******************************************/
/*************** prog322.c **************/
/*******************************************/

# include<stdio.h>
void main()
{
    int number ;
    do
    {
      printf("\n Input a number 20 to break: ");
      scanf("%d",&number) ;
      if(number < 0 )
        /* Condition true control back to scanf() */
        continue;
      printf("\n Number = %d",number);
    } while(number !=20) ;
}
```

Program 19.

```
/*******************************************/
/*************** prog323.c ***************/
/*******************************************/

# include<stdio.h>

void main()
{
    int number ;
    do
    {
      printf("\n Input a number 20 to break: ");
      scanf("%d",&number) ;
      if(number < 0 )
        /* Condition true control back to scanf() */
```

(Contd.)

```
        continue ;
      printf(" Number = %d",number);
      goto number ;
    } while(number !=20) ;
number:
    printf("\n WELCOME AT SCO UNIX 'C'");
}
```

Program 20.

```
/******************************************/
/**************   prog33.c   *************/
/******************************************/

/* Find greatest of 3 numbers */

# include<stdio.h>

void main()
{
    int a , b , c ;

    printf("\n Enter value for a , b ,c ; ") ;
    scanf("%d %d %d", &a,&b,&c) ;

    if ( a > b )
      if ( a > c )
        printf(" \n a is gratest = %d",a) ;
    if ( a < b )
      if ( b > c )
        printf(" \n b is gratest = %d",b) ;
    if ( a < b )
      if ( c > b )
        printf(" \nc is gratest = %d",c) ;
    if ( a > b )
      if ( b < c )
        if ( a < c )
          printf(" \n c is gratest  = %d",c) ;
}
```

Program 21.

```
/*****************************************/
/*************   prog34.c   ***************/
/*****************************************/

/* Summation of even and odd numbers between 0 and
100 */

# include<stdio.h>

void main()
{
    int sum ;
    int i ;
    int choice ;

    printf("\nEnter choice 1 = odd , 0 = even: ") ;
    scanf("%d", &choice ) ;

    /* Summation of even number section */

    if ( choice == 0 )
    {
    printf("\n Even number  Successive Summation");
      sum = 0 ;
      for( i = 0 ; i <= 100 ; i += 2 )
      {
        sum += i ;
        printf("\n  %4d          %4d ",i, sum);
        sleep(10);
      }
      printf("\n Even Number Sum Between 0 and 100-
      >%d",sum);
    }

    /*************** end ****************/

    /*  Summation of odd number section */

    else
    {
```

(Contd.)

```
    printf("\n Odd number Successive Summation ");
    sum = 0 ;
    for( i = 1; i <= 100 ; i+=2 )
    {
      sum += i ;
      printf("\n  %4d %4d ",i, sum);
      sleep(10);   /* Evaluation done in slow
                        manner */
    }
    printf("\n Odd Number Sum Between 0 and 100-
    >%d",sum);
  }
  /*************** end ***************/
}
```

Program 22.

```
/*******************************************/
/***************  prog35.c ***************/
/*******************************************/

# include<stdio.h>
# include<stdlib.h>
void main()
{
    char fir_name[20] ;
    char mid_name[20] ;
    char sir_name[20] ;
    char ful_name[60] ;
    char choice ;

    printf("\n Input choice f-m-s-n: ") ;
    choice = getchar() ;
    choice = toupper(choice) ;

    if ( choice == 'F' )
    {
      printf(" \nInput first name: ") ;
      scanf("%s",fir_name ) ;
    }
    else if ( choice == 'M' )
    {
```

(Contd.)

```
    printf(" \nInput middle  Name: ") ;
    scanf("%s",mid_name ) ;
   }
   else if ( choice == 'S' )
   {
    printf(" \nInput sir name: ") ;
    scanf("%s",sir_name ) ;
   }
   else if ( choice == 'N' )
   {
    printf(" \nInput full name: ") ;
    gets(ful_name ) ;
   }
   else
   {
    printf("\n Your choice is wrong ");
    printf("\n Thanking You ");
   }
}
```

Program 23.

```
/*****************************************/
/*************** prog36.c ***************/
/*****************************************/

# include<stdio.h>
void main()
{
   int result ;
   int choice ;

   printf(" \n Enter choice: ");
   scanf("%d",&choice);
   printf(" Sub = %d \n Sum = %d",sub(), sum());
   result = choice ? sum () + sub () : sum () -
             sub () ;
   printf("\n Result = %d", result) ;

}

/* Function definition */
```

(Contd.)

```
int sum ()
{
    int i ;
    int s ;
    s = 0 ;
    for (i = 0 ; i < 100 ; i += 2 )
    {
      s += i ;
    }
    return (s) ;  /* Assign value of s to sum() */
}

/* Function definition */
int sub ()
{
    int i ;
    int s ;
    s = 0 ;
    for (i = 1 ; i < 100 ; i += 2 )
    {
      s += i ;
    }
    return (s) ;  /* Assign svalue to sub() */
}
```

Program 24.

```
/*******************************************/
/**************  prog37.c  ***************/
/*******************************************/

# include<stdio.h>

void main()
{
    int x , y ;
    int result ;
    char choice ;

    x = 125 ;
    y = 24 ;
```

(Contd.)

```
while(1)
{
  printf("\n Enter choice: ") ;
  choice = getchar() ;

switch(choice)
  {
  case '-' :
    printf("\n x = %d",x);
    printf("\n y = %d",y);
    printf("\n Demo of '-' operator ");
    result = x - y ;
    printf("\n Difference of two numbers =
    %d",result);
    printf("\nPress a key");
    getchar();
    break ;

  case '+' :
    printf("\n x = %d",x);
    printf("\n y = %d",y);
    printf("\n Demo of '+' operator ");
    result = x + y ;
    printf("\n Summation  of two numbers =
    %d",result);
    printf("\nPress a key");
    getchar();
    break ;

  case '*' :
    printf("\n x = %d",x);
    printf("\n y = %d",y);
    printf("\n Demo of '*' operator ");
    result = x * y ;
    printf("\n Multiplication of two numbers =
    %d",result);
    printf("\nPress a key");
    getchar();
    break ;

  case '/' :
    printf("\n x = %d",x);
```

(Contd.)

```
        printf("\n y = %d",y);
        printf("\n Demo of '/' operator ");
        result = x / y ;
        printf("\n Division of two numbers =
        %d",result);
        printf("\nPress a key");
        getchar();
        break ;

      case '%' :
        printf("\n x = %d",x);
        printf("\n y = %d",y);
        printf("\n Demo of '%; operator ");
        result = x % y ;
        printf("\n Remainder  = %d",result);
        printf("\nPress a key");
        getchar();
        break ;

      default :
        printf(" \n Wrong choice ");
        printf("\nPress a key");
        getchar();
        exit(0) ;
      }
    }
}
```

Program 25.

```
/*******************************************/
/*************** prog38.c ****************/
/*******************************************/

# include<stdio.h>

void test_operator(char , int , int ); /* prototype
*/

  void main()
      {
      int a , b ;
```

(Contd.)

```
    int result ;
    char choice ;

    a = 125 ;
    b = 24 ;
printf("\n a = %d", a);
printf("\n b = %d", b);
    while(1)
    {
    printf("\n Enter choice: ") ;
    choice = getchar() ;
    test_operator(choice, a, b);
    }
   }

  /* Definition of function */

 void test_operator(char ch, int x , int y )
   {
    int result ;
    if (ch == '-')
 {
  printf("\n Demo of '-' operator ");
  result = x - y ;
  printf("\n Difference of two numbers =
  %d",result);
  printf("\nPress a key");
  getchar();
 }
    else if (ch == '+')
 {
  printf("\n Demo of '+' operator ");
  result = x + y ;
  printf("\n Summation  of two numbers =
  %d",result);
  printf("\nPress a key");
  getchar();
 }
    else if (ch == '*')
 {
  printf("\n Demo of '*' operator ");
  result = x * y ;
```

(Contd.)

```
printf("\n Multiplication of two numbers =
 %d",result);
printf("\nPress a key");
getchar();
}
 else if (ch == '/')
{
printf("\n Demo of '/' operator ");
 result = x / y ;
printf("\n Division of two numbers =
 %d",result);
printf("\nPress a key");
getchar();
}
 else if ( ch == '%')
{
printf("\n Demo of '%' operator ");
 result = x % y ;
printf("\n Remainder = %d",result);
printf("\nPress a key");
getchar();
}
 else
{
printf(" \n Wrong choice ");
printf("\nPress a key");
getchar();
exit(0);
}
}
```

Program 26.

```
/*****************************************/
/*************** prog39.c **************/
/*****************************************/

# include<stdio.h>

void main()
{
    int choice ;
```

(Contd.)

```
    while(1)
    {
      printf(" \n Enter choice: ");
      scanf("%d",&choice);
      demo(choice);
    }
}

/* Definition of function demo()  */

demo(int ch )
{
    switch(ch)
    {
    case 1:
      printf("\n Choice Number: %d",ch) ;

    case 2:
      printf("\n Choice Number: %d",ch) ;

    case 3:
      printf("\n Choice Number: %d",ch) ;

    case 4:
      printf("\n Choice Number: %d",ch) ;
      break;

    case 5:
      printf("\n WELCOME SIR") ;
      break ;

    default :
      exit(0);
    }
}
```

Section III

Program 1.

```
/* prog51.c */

# include<stdio.h>
void main()
{
    int List [10] = {
      00,11,22,33,44,55,66,77,88,99};
    int i;
    for (i = 0; i < 10; i++)
    {
      printf("\n List[%d] = %d", i, List[i]);
    }
}
```

Program 2.

```
/* prog510.c */

# include<stdio.h>
# include<string.h>

void main ()
{
    char arraya[9] = {
      "Language"};
    char arrayb[3];
    strcpy (arrayb, "Compiler"); /* Overwrites */
    printf("\n Output printed by arraya: %s",
    arraya);
```

(Contd.)

```
    printf("\n Output printed by arrayb: %s",
    arrayb);
}
```

Program 3.

```
/* prog511.c */

# include<stdio.h>

int show_value(int value[], int number_of_element)
{
    int i;
    int sum =0;
    printf("\n expression = value");
    for (i =0; i < number_of_element; i++)
    {
      printf("\n   value[%d] = %d",i, value[i]);
      sum += value[i];
    }
    return (sum);
}

void main()
{
    int parameter[10] = {
      70, 80, 90,100, 200,300 };
    int result;
    result = show_value(parameter, 6);
    printf("\n Summation = %d", result);
}
```

Program 4.

```
/* prog512.c */

# include<stdio.h>

void gets1(char s[])
{
    int i = 0 ;
    char ch;
```

(Contd.)

```
    ch = getchar();
    while(ch !='\n').
    {
      s[i] = ch;
      i++;
      ch = getchar();
    }
    s[i] = '\0';
}
void puts1(char s[])
{
    char ch;
    int i = 0;
    for ( i= 0; s[i] != '\0'; i++)
    {
      ch = s[i];
      putchar(ch);
    }
}
void main()
{
    char string [256];
    gets1(string);
    puts1(string);
}
```

Program 5.

```
/* prog513.c */

# include<stdio.h>
void main()
{
    char string[256];
    int i;
    for(i =0; i < 26; i++)
    {
      string[i] = 'A'+i;
    }
    string[i] = '\0';
    printf("\n The string is : %s", string);
}
```

Program 6.

```
/* prog514.c */

# include<stdio.h>
void main()
{
    char string[256];
    int i;
    for(i =0; i < 26; i++)
    {
      string[i] = 'A'+i;
    }
    string[10] = '\0';
    printf("\n The string is : %s", string);
}
```

Program 7.

```
/* prog515.c */

# include<stdio.h>

void main()
{
    int vector1 [10] = {
      4,5,6,7,8,9,12,13,14,90 };
    int vector2 [10] = {
     10,12,13,14,15,16,17,18,19,20};
    int result [10 ] ;
    char choice ;
    int i ;
    do
    {
      printf("\n Enter Choice \n A=Addition \n
      S=Subtraction \n M=Multiplication \n Choice
      is:");
      choice = getchar() ;
      choice = toupper(choice) ;

      switch(choice)
      {
```

(Contd.)

```
case 'A' :
  printf("\n Addition operation ");
  for( i = 0 ; i < 10 ; i++ )
  {
    result [i] = vector1[i] + vector2[i] ;
  }
  for( i = 0 ; i < 10 ; i++ )
  {
    printf("\n %d",result [i] );
  }
  printf("\n Press a key");
  getchar() ;
  break ;

case 'S' :
  printf("\n Subtraction operation ");
  for( i = 0 ; i < 10 ; i++ )
  {
    result [i] = vector1[i] - vector2[i] ;
  }
  for( i = 0 ; i < 10 ; i++ )
  {
    printf("\n %d",result [i] );
  }
  printf("\n Press a key");
  getchar() ;
  break ;

case 'M' :
  printf("\n Multiplication operation ");
  for( i = 0 ; i < 10 ; i++ )
  {
    result [i] = vector1[i] * vector2[i] ;
  }
  for( i = 0 ; i < 10 ; i++ )
  {
    printf("\n %d",result [i] );
  }
  printf("\n Press a key");
  getchar() ;
  break ;
```

(Contd.)

```
        default :
          printf("\n Choice is Wrong ");
          printf("\n Press a key");
          getchar() ;
          exit(0);
        }
      } while (( choice == 'A' )
          || ( choice == 'S' )
          || (choice == 'M')) ;
}
```

Program 8.

```
/* prog516.c */

# include<stdio.h>

void main()
{
    int choice ;
    char list [11] = {
      'T','O','M',' ','A','L','T','E','R','\0'};
    printf("\n Enter Choice: ") ;
    scanf("%d",&choice) ;
    printf("\n Position : %d Value : %c",choice+1,
    list[choice]);
}
```

Program 9.

```
/* prog517.c */

# include<stdio.h>

void main()
{
    int num[5][3] ;
    int i ;
    int j ;

    for( i = 0 ; i < 5 ; i ++ )
    {
```

(Contd.)

```
    for ( j = 0; j < 3 ; j ++ )
    {
      num[i][j] = i*j ;
    }
  }

  for( i = 0 ; i < 5 ; i ++ )
  {
    printf("\n Row = %3d",i+1);
    for ( j = 0; j < 3 ; j ++ )
    {
      printf("\n num[%d][%d] = %6d  ",i,j,
      num[i][j]);
    }
  }
}
```

Program 10.

```
/* prog518.c */

# include<stdio.h>

void main()
{
    int num[5][3] ;
    int i ;
    int j ;
    for( i = 0 ; i < 5 ; i ++ )
    {
      for ( j = 0; j < 3 ; j ++ )
      {
        num[i][j] = i*j ;
      }
    }
    printf("\nAddress  Subscript  value \n");
    for( i = 0 ; i < 5 ; i ++ )
    {
      for ( j = 0; j < 3 ; j ++ )
      {
        printf("\n %x  | num[%d][%d]  | %d
        ",&num[i][j],
```

(Contd.)

```
            i,j, num[i][j]);
        }
      }
}
```

Program 11.

```
/* prog519.c */

# include<stdio.h>
# include<stdlib.h>

void main()
{
    int matrix1[3][4] ;
    int matrix2[3][4] ;
    int result[3][4] ;
    int i , j ;
    printf("\nGeneration of  Matrix of Size 3x4 in
    Progress ");

printf("\n*******************************************");
    printf("\n MATRIX ONE");
    for( i = 0 ; i < 3 ; i++ )
    {
      printf("\n") ;
      for ( j = 0 ; j < 4 ; j++ )
      {
        matrix1[i][j] = rand();
        printf("%6d  ",matrix1[i][j] ) ;
      }
    }
    printf("\n MATRIX SECOND ");
    for( i = 0 ; i < 3 ; i++ )
    {
      printf("\n") ;
      for ( j = 0 ; j < 4 ; j++ )
      {
        matrix2[i][j] = rand();
        printf("%6d  ",matrix2[i][j] ) ;
      }
    }
```

(Contd.)

```
/* Summation section */

printf("\n MATRIX SECOND ");
for( i = 0 ; i < 3 ; i++ )
{
  for ( j = 0 ; j < 4 ; j++ )
  {
  result[i][j] = matrix1[i][j] + matrix2[i][j];
  }
}

/* Output */

printf("\n\n\n Summation of two  Matrices ");
printf("\n Output Matrix Of Size 3x4 ");
printf("\n");
for( i = 0 ; i < 3 ; i++ )
{
  printf("\n") ;
  for ( j = 0 ; j < 4 ; j++ )
  {
    printf("%6d", result[i][j]) ;
  }
}
printf("\n");
printf("\n Press a key");
getchar() ;
}
```

Program 12.

```
/* prog52.c */

# include<stdio.h>

main()
{
    int Count[] = {
    11, 22, 33, 44, 55, 66, 77, 88, 99, 100, 200 };
    printf("\n %d", Count [4]);
}
```

Program 13.

```
/* prog520.c */

# include<stdio.h>
# include<stdlib.h>

void main()
{
    int matrix1[5][5] = {
                  { 1,1,1,1,1 },
                  { 2,2,2,2,2 },
                  { 3,3,3,3,3 },
                  { 4,4,4,4,4 },
                  { 5,5,5,5,5 }  };
    int matrix2[5][5] = {
                  { 0,0,0,0,0 },
                  { 6,6,6,6,6 },
                  { 7,7,7,7,7 },
                  { 8,8,8,8,8 },
                  { 9,9,9,9,9 }  };
    int i   j ;
    int result[5][5] ;
    char choice ;
    do
    {
      printf("\n Enter Choice \n A=Addition \n
      S=Subtraction \n N=Break \n Choice is:");
      choice = getchar() ;
      choice = toupper(choice) ;
      if(choice == 'A')
      {

        printf("\n");

        for( i = 0 ; i < 5 ; i++ )
        {
          for ( j = 0 ; j < 5 ; j++ )
      {
      result[i][j] = matrix1[i][j] + matrix2[i][j] ;
      }
        }
```

(Contd.)

```
    /* Output */

    printf("\n Output Matrix Addition of Two
    Matrcies  ");
    printf("\n");
    for( i = 0 ; i < 5 ; i++ )
    {
      printf("\n") ;
      for ( j = 0 ; j < 5 ; j++ )
      {
        printf("%6d", result[i][j]) ;
      }
    }
    printf("\n");
    printf("\n Press a key ");
    getchar() ;
  }
  else
    if(choice == 'S')
    {

      printf("\n");

      for( i = 0 ; i < 5 ; i++ )
      {
        for ( j = 0 ; j < 5 ; j++ )
  {
  result[i][j] = matrix1[i][j] - matrix2[i][j] ;
  }
      }

      /* Output */

      printf("\n Output Matrix Subtraction of
      Two Matrcies  ");
      printf("\n");

      for( i = 0 ; i < 5 ; i++ )
      {
        printf("\n") ;
        for ( j = 0 ; j < 5 ; j++ )
        {
          printf("%6d", result[i][j]) ;
```

(Contd.)

```
            }
          }
          printf("\n");
          printf("\n Press a key ");
          getchar() ;
        }
        else if(choice == 'N')
        {
          printf("\n Choice is wrong ");
          printf("\n Press a key to exit ");
          getchar() ;
          exit(0) ;
        }
    } while (choice !='N');
}
```

Program 14.

```
/* prog521.c */

# include<stdio.h>

void main()
{
    char string[5][16] = {
                          "TOM ALTER",
                          "JERRY",
                          "TILLY",
                          "MONGIA",
                          "TENDULKAR"
                          };

    int i ;
    printf("\n Subscript Variable Starting Address
    String");
    for ( i = 0 ; i < 5 ; i++ )
    {
      printf("\n");
      printf("string[%d][6]",i);
      printf("%18x",&string[i]);
      printf(" %12s",string[i]);
    }
```

(Contd.)

```
    printf("\n Press a key");
    getchar() ;
}
```

Program 15.

```
/* prog522.c */

# include<stdio.h>
void main()
{
    char string[5][16] = {
                          "TOM ALTER",
                          "JERRY",
                          "TILLY",
                          "MONGIA",
                          "TENDULKAR"
                          };

    int i ;
    int j ;
    for ( i = 0 ; i < 5 ; i++ )
    {
      printf("\n");
      printf("string[%d][6]     ",i);
      for( j = 0; j < 16 ;  j++)
      {
        printf("%c",string[i][j]);
      }
      printf("\\0");
    }
    printf("\n Press a key");
    getchar() ;
}
```

Program 16.

```
/* prog523.c */

# include<stdio.h>

void main()
{
```

(Contd.)

```
    float m[5][5][5] ;
    int i , j, k ;
    for( i = 0 ; i < 5 ; i++ )
    {
      for ( j = 0 ; j < 5 ; j++ )
      {
        for ( k = 0 ; k < 5 ; k++ )
        {
          m[i][j][k] = 4.5*i * j / (k + 1 ) ;
        }
      }
    }

    /* Output section */

    for( i = 0 ; i < 5 ; i++ )
    {
      printf("\n");
      for ( j = 0 ; j < 5 ; j++ )
      {
        printf("\n");
        for ( k = 0 ; k < 5 ; k++ )
        {
          printf("\n m[%d][%d][%d]  = ",i,j,k);
          printf("%3.2f",m[i][j][k]) ;
        }
      }
    }
}
```

Program 17.

```
/* prog53.c */

# include<stdio.h>

main()
{
    int Counter[10] = {
          11, 22, 33, 44  };
    int i;
    for (i = 0; i < 10; i ++)
```

(Contd.)

```
    {
      printf("\nCounter [%d] = %d",i, Counter [i]);
    }
}
```

Program 18.

```
/* prog54.c */

# include<stdio.h>

main()
{
    int array_pointer[10] = {
         11, 22, 33, 44, 55, 66, 77, 88, 99  };
    printf("\n %d", array_pointer [6]);
}
```

Program 19.

```
/* prog55.c */

# include<stdio.h>

main()
{
    int array_pointer[10] = {
            11, 22, 33, 44, 55, 66, 77, 88, 99, 100
      };
    int i;
    printf("\n Index Address   Value");
    for (i =0; i< 10; i++)
    {
      printf("\n %d %X  %d",i,&array_pointer[i],
array_pointer [i]);
    }
}
```

Program 20.

```
/* prog56.c */

# include<stdio.h>

main()
{
    int array_pointer[10] = {
          11, 22, 33, 44, 55, 66, 77, 88, 99, 100
                                    };
    int *pointer;
    pointer = & array_pointer[0];
    printf("\nCell Address: %X Cell Information:
    %d",pointer, *pointer);
    pointer =  array_pointer;
    printf("\nCell Address: %X Cell Information:
    %d",pointer, *pointer);
    pointer++;
    pointer++;
    pointer++;
    printf("\nCell Address: %X Cell Information:
    %d",pointer, *pointer);
}
```

Program 21.

```
/* prog57.c */

# include<stdio.h>

void main()
{
    char carray [12] = {
                          "RAM BAHADUR"  };
    char *carray1;
    int i = 0;
    carray1 = carray;
    printf("\n Index Address Value");
    while(*carray1 != '\0')
    {
      printf("\n %d %X %c",i,carray1, *carray1);
```

(Contd.)

```
        carray1++;
        i++;
      }
  }
```

Program 22.

```
  /* prog58.c */

  # include<stdio.h>

  void main()
  {
      char carray [12] = {
                              "RAM BAHADUR"    };
      char *carray1;
      int i = 0;
      carray1 = carray;
      carray[0] = 66;
      printf("\n Index Address Value");
      while(*carray1 != '\0')
      {
        printf("\n %d %X %c",i,carray1, *carray1);
        carray1++;
        i++;
      }
  }
```

Program 23.

```
  /* prog59.c */

  # include<stdio.h>

  void main()
  {
      char carray [12];
      char *carray1;
      int i = 0;

      carray[0] = 'R';
      carray[1] = 'A';
```

(Contd.)

```
    carray[2] = 'M';
    carray[3] = ' ';
    carray[4] = 'B';
    carray[5] = 'A';
    carray[6] = 'H';
    carray[7] = 'A';
    carray[8] = 'D';
    carray[9] = 'U';
    carray[10]= 'R';
    carray1 = carray;
    printf("\n Index Address Value");
    while(*carray1 != '\0')
    {
      printf("\n %d %X %c",i,carray1, *carray1);
      carray1++;
      i++;
    }
}
```

Program 24.

```
/* strcat.c */

# include<stdio.h>

char *strcat1(char *target, const char *source)
{
    char *original = target;
    while(*target)
      target++;
    while (*target++= *source++);
    return(original);
}

main()
{
    char Name[256]="Ram Bahadur ";
    char Title[256]="Patel";
    strcat1(Name, Title);
    puts(Name);
}
```

Program 25.

```
/* strchr.c */

# include<stdio.h>
char *strchr1(const char *string, int letter)
{
    while((*string != letter)&&(*string))
      string++;
    return(string);
}

main()
{
    char string [256] ={
              "EXPERT DATA STRUCTURES WITH C++"  };
    char *pointer;
    pointer = strchr1(string, 'A');
    if (*pointer)
      printf("\n First occurence of 'A' is at
      distance (offset): %d", pointer-string);
    else
      printf("\n Character 'A' is not found");
}
```

Program 26.

```
/* strchr_i.c */

# include<stdio.h>
int strchr_I(const char *string, int letter)
{
    char *original = string;
    while((*string != letter)&&(*string))
      string++;
    return(string - original);
}

main()
{
    char string [256] ={
         "EXPERT DATA STRUCTURES WITH C++"    };
```

(Contd.)

```
    int index;
    index = strchr_I(string, 'A');
    if (index == strlen(string))
      printf("\n Character 'A' is not found");
    else
      printf("Character is found at index:
      %d",index);
}
```

Program 27.

```
/* strcmp.c */

# include<stdio.h>
# include<string.h>

int strcmp1(const char *s1, const char *s2)
{
    while((*s1== *s2) && (*s1))
    {
      s1++;
      s2++;
    }
    if((*s1 == *s2) && (! *s1)) /* Same string */
      return (0);
    else
      if ((*s1) && (! *s2))
                        /* Same but s1 is is longer */
        return (-1);
      else
        if ((*s2) && (! *s1))
                        /* Same but s2 is longer */

          return(1);
        else
          return ((*s1 > *s2) ? -1 : 1);
}

main()
{
    char s1[256] = {
                        "Rachita" };
```

(Contd.)

```
    char s2[256] = {
                    "RachitaRB" };
    char s3[256] = {
                    "RBRachita" };
    printf("\n Comparing string Rachita and
    Rachita: %d",strcmp1(s1, s1));
    printf("\n Comparing string Rachita and
    RachitaRB: %d",strcmp1(s1, s2));
    printf("\n Comparing string Rachita and
    RBRachita: %d",strcmp1(s1, s3));
}
```

Program 28.

```
/* strcpy.c */

# include <stdio.h>


char *strcpy1(char *dest, const char *source)
{
    while (*dest++= *source++);
    return(dest-1);
}

main()
{
    char dest[256]= {
      "EXPERT DATA STRUCTURES WITH C++"  };
    char source[256]=" ";
    printf("\n Input Source string: ");
    gets(source);

    strcpy1(dest,source);
    puts(dest);
}
```

Program 29.

```
/* strdup.c */

# include<stdio.h>
```

(Contd.)

```
# include<string.h>
# include<malloc.h>

char *strdup1(const char *s1)
{
    char *pointer;
    if ((pointer = malloc(strlen(s1))))
                                /* Allocate buffer */
      strcpy (pointer, s1);
    return(pointer);
}

void main()
{
    char string [256] = {
                            "Work is Worship"};
    printf("\nDuplicate: %s",strdup1(string));
}
```

Program 30.

```
/* streql.c */

# include<stdio.h>

int streql1 (char *str1, char *str2)
{
    while(( * str1 == *str2)&&(*str1))
    {
      str1++;
      str2++;
    }
    return ((*str1== NULL)&&(*str2 == NULL));
}

void main()
{

    printf("\n Testing Rachita and Rachita: %d\n",
    streql1("Rachita", "Rachita"));
    printf("\n Testing rachita and Rachita: %d\n",
    streql1("rachita", "Rachita"));
```

(Contd.)

```
    printf("\n Testing Rachitarb and Rachita:
    %d\n", streql1("Rachitarb", "Rachita"));
}
```

Program 31.

```
/* strieql.c */

# include<stdio.h>
# include<ctype.h>

int strieql1 (char *str1, char *str2)
{
while((toupper(*str1) == toupper(*str2))&&(*str1))
    {
      str1++;
      str2++;
    }
    return ((*str1== NULL)&&(*str2 == NULL));
}

void main()
{
    printf("\n Testing Rachita and Rachita: %d\n",
    strieql1("Rachita", "Rachita"));
    printf("\n Testing rachita and Rachita: %d\n",
    strieql1("rachita", "Rachita"));
    printf("\n Testing Rachitarb and Rachita:
    %d\n", strieql1("Rachitarb", "Rachita"));
}
```

Program 32.

```
/* strlen.c */

int strlen1 (const char *str)
{
    int length=0;
    int i=0;
    while (str[i] != '\0')
    {
      i++;
```

(Contd.)

```
        length ++;
      }
      return (length);
  }

  # include<stdio.h>

  void main()
  {
      char str[256] = "Expert Data Structures With
      C++";
      int Length ;
      Length = strlen1(str);
      printf("\n Length = %d", Length);
  }
```

Program 33.

```
/* strncat.c */

# include<stdio.h>
char *strncat1(char *dest, const char * source, int
n)
{
    char *original = dest;
    int i =0;
    while (*dest) dest++;
    while((i++ < n) && (*dest ++ = *source++));

    if ( i> n)
      *dest = NULL;
    return(original);
}

main()
{
    char Name[256] = "Rachita ";
    char Middle [256] = "and Misthi";
    strncat1 (Name, Middle, 3);
    puts (Name);

}
```

Program 34.

```
/* strncmp.c */

# include<stdio.h>
# include<string.h>

int strncmp1(const char *s1, const char *s2, int n)
{
    int i=0;
    while((*s1== *s2) && (*s1) && (i < n))
    {
      s1++;
      s2++;
      i++;
    }
    if ( i == n) /* same string */
      return (0);

    if((*s1 == *s2) && (! *s1)) /* Same string */
      return (0);
    else
      if ((*s1) && (! *s2))
                    /* Same but s1 is is longer */
        return (-1);
      else
        if ((*s2) && (! *s1))
                    /* Same but s2 is longer */

          return(1);
        else
          return ((*s1 > *s2) ? -1 : 1);
}

main()
{
    char s1[256] = {
                    "Rachita"   };
    char s2[256] = {
                    "RachitaRB"   };
    char s3[256] = {
                    "RBRachita"   };
```

(Contd.)

```
    printf("\n Comparing string Rachita and
    Rachita: %d",strncmpl(s1, s1, 4));
    printf("\n Comparing string Rachita and
    RachitaRB: %d",strncmpl(s1, s2,8));
    printf("\n Comparing string Rachita and
    RBRachita: %d",strncmpl(s1, s3,3));
}
```

Program 35.

```
/* strrchr.c */

# include<stdio.h>
char *strrchrl(const char *string, int letter)
{
    char *pointer = NULL;

    while(*string)
    {
      if(*string ==letter)
        pointer = string;
      string++;
    }

    return(pointer);
}

main()
{
    char string [256] ={
        "EXPERT DATA STRUCTURES WITH C++"    };
    char *pointer;
    if (pointer =strrchrl(string, 'H'))
      // if (*pointer)
      printf("\n Rightmost occurence of 'H' is at
      distance (offset): %d", pointer-string);
    else
      printf("\n Character 'A' is not found");
}
```

Program 36.

```
/* strrchr_i.c */

# include<stdio.h>
# include<string.h>

int strrchr_i(const char *string, int letter)
{
    char *pointer = NULL;
    char *original = string ;

    while(*string)
    {
      if(*string == letter)
        pointer = string;
      string++;
    }

return((*pointer)? pointer - original : string -
original);
}

main()
{
    char string [256] ={
              "EXPERT DATA STRUCTURES WITH C++"  };
    int index;
    index = strrchr_i(string, 'H');
    if (index == strlen(string))
      printf("\n Character 'H' is not found");
    else
      printf("\n Rightmost occurence of 'H' is at
      index: %d", index);
}
```

Program 37.

```
/* strspn.c */

# include<stdio.h>
```

(Contd.)

```
int strspn1(const char *s1, const char *s2)
{
    int i=0, j=0;
    for (i =0; *s1; i++, s1++)
    {
      for (j =0; s2[j]; j++)
        if(*s1 == s2 [j])
          break;
      if(s2[j] == NULL)
        break;
    }
    return (i);
}
void main()
{
    printf("\n Search for Rachita in
    RachitaRBPatel: %d",
    strspn1("RachitaRBPatel","Rachita"));
}
```

Program 38.

```
/*  strstr.c */

# include<stdio.h>

char *strstr1(const char *s1, const char *s2)
{
    int i, j, k;
    for(i =0; s1[i]; i++)
      for(j = i, k =0; s1[j] == s2[k]; j++, k++)
        if(!s2 [k+1])
          return(s1+i);
    return(NULL);
}

void main()
{
    printf("\n Looking for Rach in Rachita %s",(
    strstr1("Rachita","Rach")) ? "Found" : "Not
    found");
}
```

Program 39.

```
/*  strstr_i.c *

# include<stdio.h>

int strstr_index(const char *s1, const char *s2)
{
    int i, j, k;
    for(i =0; s1[i]; i++)
      for(j = i, k = 0; s1[j] == s2[k]; j++, k++)
        if(!s2 [k+1])
          return(i);
    return(i);
}

void main()
{
    char String[256] ={
                        "chitraRachitaRachita" };
    char Substring[256] = {
                            "Rach" };

    printf("\n Looking for Rach in
    chitraRachitaRachita: %d",(
    strstr_index(String,Substring)));
}
```

Program 40.

```
/* strxfrm.c */

# include<stdio.h>
main()
{

    char Buffer [256] = "Expert Data Structures
    With C++";
    char Target[256];
    int Length;
    Length = strxfrm(Target, Buffer,
    sizeof(Buffer));
```

(Contd.)

```
    printf("\n Length %dTarget %s Buffer %s",
Length, Target, Buffer);
}
```

Program 41.

```
/*  strstr_cnt.c */

# include<stdio.h>

int strstr_cnt(const char *s1, const char *s2)
{
    int i, j, k, count =0;
    for(i =0; s1[i]; i++)
      for(j = i, k = 0; s1[j] == s2[k]; j++, k++)
        if(!s2 [k+1])
count ++;
return(count);
}

void main()
{
char String[256] ={"RachitaRachitaRachitaRachita"};
char Substring[256] = {"Rach"};

    printf("\n Looking for Rach in
    RachitaRachitaRachitaRachita %d",(
    strstr_cnt(String,Substring)));
```

Section IV

Program 1.

```
/* Use of va_arg and va_end parameter */
/* ADD_VARG.C */

# include <stdio.h>
# include <stdarg.h>

double add_values(char *str, ...)
  {
  va_list marker;

  double result = 0.0;

  va_start(marker, str);  /* mark first
  additional argument */

  while (*str)              /* examine each
  character in the string */
     {
  if (*str == '%')    /* if not a %_ format
  specifier, skip it */
    {
      switch (*(++str))
        {
           case 'd': result += va_arg(marker,
           int);
           break;
           case 'f': result += va_arg(marker,
           double);
```

(Contd.)

```
            break;
         }
      }
    str++;
    }

  va_end(marker);
  return(result);
}

void main(void)
 {
   double result;
   int x,y;
   float i,j,k;
   printf("\n Input the values for x, y
   integer:");
   scanf("%d%d",&x,&y);
   printf("\n Input the values for i, j, k
   floating:");
   scanf("%f%f%f",&i,&j,&k);

   result = add_values("%f%d%f%d%f", i,x,j,y,k);
   printf("\n %f+%d+%f+%d+%f = %f ", i,x,j,y,k,
   result);
 }
```

Program 2.

```
/* arg_add.c */

#include <stdio.h>
#include <stdarg.h>

double add_values(double value, ...)
 {
   va_list argument_ptr;
   double result = 0.0;

   if (value != 0.0)
     {
       result += value;
```

(Contd.)

```
        va_start(argument_ptr, value);

      while ((value = va_arg(argument_ptr,
      double)) != 0.0)
      result += value;

      va_end(argument_ptr);
     }
   return(result);
 }

void main(void)
 {
   double result;
   double x,y;
   double i,j,k;
   printf("\n Input the values for x, y double:");
   scanf("%lf%lf",&x,&y);
   printf("\n Input the values for i, j, k
   double:");
   scanf("%lf%lf%lf",&i,&j,&k);

   result = add_values(i, x, j, y, k, 0.0);
   printf("\n %lf+%lf+%lf+%lf+%lf = %lf ", i, x,
   j, y, k, result);
 }
```

Program 3.

```
/*****************************************/
/***********    argproto.c    ************/
/*****************************************/

# include<stdio.h>

void inter_change(int x , int y ) ; /* Prototype */

void main()
{
   int x ;
   int y ;
   x = 20 ;
```

(Contd.)

```
    y = 30 ;
    printf("\n\nValues before function call ");
    printf("\n\nx = %d \ny = %d",x,y);
    inter_change(x,y);
    printf("\n\nValues after  function call ");
    printf("\n\nx = %d \ny = %d",x,y);
}

// Definition of function

void inter_change( int a , int b)
{
    int temp ;
    temp = a ;
    a = b ;
    b = temp ;
}
```

Program 4.

```
/*******************************************/
/************    compare.c   *************/
/*******************************************/

# include<stdio.h>

int *compare( int , int * ,  int ) ; /* prototype
*/
int en ;
void main()
{
    int list[10] = {
    12,16,18,19,14,20,94,78,30 };
    int num ;
    int size ;
    int *ar ;
    printf("\n Enter the size of array: ");
    scanf("%d",&size);
    printf("\n Enter number want to  match: ");
    scanf("%d",&num);

    ar = compare(num,list,size) ; /* invoke */
```

(Contd.)

```
    if(ar)
    {
      printf("\n Element number = %d",en);
    }
    else
    {
      printf("No Match Found ");
    }
    getchar();
}
// Function definition

int *compare(int num, int *array , int size)
{
    register int i ;
    i = 0 ;
    en = i ;
    while( (num != array[i]) && (i < size) )
    {
      i++ ;
      en = i;
    }
    return(&array[i-1]) ;
}
```

Program 5.

```
/*****************************************/
/*************    complex.c    ***********/
/*****************************************/

/* complex number addition */

# include<stdio.h>

struct complex1
{
    float x ;
    float y ;
};

typedef struct complex1 com ;
```

(Contd.)

```
com complex_fun(com  , com ); /* Prototype **/
void main()
{
    com  plex1 , plex2 , plex3  ;
    plex1.x = 40.3 ;
    plex1.y = 30.3 ;

    plex2.x = 0.7 ;
    plex2.y = 0.7 ;
    printf("\n First compex number = ");
    printf("%f + j %f ", plex1.x,plex1.y);
    printf("\n Second compex number = ");
    printf("%f + j %f ", plex2.x,plex2.y);
    plex3 = complex_fun(plex1,plex2) ;
    printf("\n Summation of compex numbers = ");
    printf("%f + j %f ", plex3.x,plex3.y);
    printf("\n Press a key");
    getchar() ;   /* control screen */
}

/* Definition of function */

com complex_fun(com l1 , com l2)
{
    com l3 ;
    l3.x = l1.x + l2.x ;
    l3.y = l1.y + l2.y ;
    return(l3);
}
```

Program 6.

```
/*****************************************/
/***********    convert.c    **************/
/*****************************************/

# include<stdio.h>
struct gin
{
    int x ;
    int y ;
};
```

(Contd.)

```
struct gin  conversion() ; /** prototype **/

void main()
{
    struct gin int_float ;
    int_float = conversion() ;
    printf("\n x = %d \n y =
    %d",int_float.x,int_float.y);
    printf("\n Press a key");
    getchar() ;   /* control screen */
}

/* Definition of function */
struct gin  conversion()
{
    struct gin rec ;
    printf("\n Enter integer part: ");
    scanf("%d",&rec.x);
    printf("\nEnter real part: ");
    scanf("%d",&rec.y);
    return(rec);
}
```

Program 7.

```
/******************************************/
/***************    env.c   ***************/
/******************************************/
# include<stdio.h>

  void main(char *env[])
    {
       int i  ;
       for( i = 0 ; env[i] ; i++)
       {
       printf("\n%s : string number :%d",
env[i],i+1);
       }
    }
```

Program 8.

```
// prog44.c

# include<stdio.h>
void main()
{
    int  n ;
    long int result ;
    printf("\n Enter a number = ");
    scanf("%d",&n);
    result = factorial(n) ;   /* Invoke function */
    printf("\n Factorial = %ld",result) ;
}

/// Definition of factorial()

factorial(int m)
{
    int fact  ;
    if ( m == 0 )
      return ( 1 );
    else
      fact = m * factorial(m-1) ;
    return (fact);
}
```

Program 9.

```
// factor.c

#include <stdio.h>

long int factorial(int value)
{
    long int result;
    if (value == 1)
    {
      printf("Returning the value 1\n");
      return(1);
    }
    else
```

(Contd.)

```
    {
      result = value * factorial(value-1);
      printf("Returning %d * factorial(%d) = %ld\n",
          value, value-1, result);
      return(result);
          //value * factorial(value-1));
    }
}

void main(void)
{
    int number;
    printf("\n Input a number: ");
    scanf("%d",& number);
    printf("The factorial of %d is %ld\n", number,
    factorial(number));
}
```

Program 10.

```
/******************************************/
/**************  filecp.c   **************/
/******************************************/
# include<stdio.h>
# include<stdlib.h>

void main(int argc, char *argv[] )
{
    int ch ;
    FILE *fp ;
    if(argc != 2 )
    {
      printf("\nYou Have Missed file  ");
      exit(0) ;
    }
      fp = fopen(argv[1], "r") ;
      if(fp == NULL)
    {
      perror("Error") ;
      exit(1);
    }
```

(Contd.)

```
    ch = getc(fp) ;
    while(ch != EOF)
    {
      putchar(ch) ;
      ch = getc(fp) ;
    }
}
```

Program 11.

```
// prog46.c

find ( int a[3] , int b )
{
    int i ;
    for( i = 0 ;  i < 3 ; i++)
      if(a[i] == 'B' )
        return (i) ;
      else
        return (-1);

}
```

Program 12.

```
// prog45.c

void fun ( int n , char *s )
{
    int i ;
    for( i = n ; i ; --i)
    {
      printf("\n%s",s) ;
      printf("%d Time ",i) ;
    }
}
```

Program 13.

```
// prog43.c

# include<stdio.h>
```

(Contd.)

```
void main()
{
    int x , y ;
    int result ;
    x = 20 ;
    y = 30 ;
    result = fun ( x, y) * x / y ;
    printf("\n x = %d",x);
    printf("\n y = %d", y);
    printf("\n Value = %d",result ) ;
}

// Definition of fun()

fun(int a , int b )
{
    int result ;
    result =  a*b ;
    return (result) ;
}
```

Program 14.

```
/*******************************************/
/************** funarray.c **************/
/*******************************************/

# include<stdlib.h>
# include<stdio.h>

void main()
{
    int data ;
    int least[100] ;
    int number , i ;
    number = 10 ;
    for( i = 0 ; i <= 10 ; i++ )
    {
      least [ i ] = (int) random()/1000 ; /*
      Generates random number */
    }
    printf(" \n Enter data to which want to see:");
    scanf("%d",&data);
```

(Contd.)

```
    printf("\n***********************************");
    printf("\nPOSITION NUMBER VALUE STORED");
    printf("\n***********************************");
    search(least, data, number);
    printf("\n***********************************");
}

// Definition  of function

search(int l[100] , int data , int number )
{
    int j ;
    j = 0 ;
    while(j <= number )
    {
      system("setcolor 4 15");
      printf("\n %4d      %4d   ",j,l[ j ]);
      if (l[j] == data )
      {
        printf("Found = %d, Position =
        %d\n",data,j);
        system(" setcolor 5 15 ");
        system ("tput cup 50,24");
        printf("\033[0m press a key");
        getchar();
        return;
      }
      j++ ;
    }
    printf("\n Not found ");
    return :
}
```

Program 15.

```
/*****************************************/
/**************   prog48.c  *************/
/*****************************************/
# include<stdio.h>

float m_payment(float  , float , int ) ;  /*
Prototype */
double powl( int , register int );
```

(Contd.)

```
void main()
{
    float A , I ;
            /* Mortage amount A, I interest rate */
    int D ;                          /* Duration is D */

    printf("\n Enter Mortage Amount = ");
    scanf("%f",&A);
    printf("\n Enter interest rate = ");
    scanf("%f",&I);
    printf("\n Enter Duration  = " );
    scanf("%d",&D);
    printf("\n Monthly Payment =
    %f",m_payment(A,I,D) );
}

/* Definition of function */

float m_payment( float a , float i , int d )
{
    float num ;
    float deno ;
    float payment ;
    num = ( a * i /12 ) ;
    deno = pow1( (1/(1+i/12)),d*12);
    payment = num / ( 1 - deno ) ;
    return(payment);
}

/* Definition of function  pow1() */

double pow1( int base, register int exponent)
{
    register int t ;
    t = 1;
    for( ; exponent ; exponent--)
    {
      t *= base ;
    }
    return(t);
}
```

Program 16.

```
// prog47.c

# include<stdio.h>

int x, y;  /* Global  variable */
float xy_power(void) ;  /* Prototype */

void main()
{
   printf("\n Enter value of x, y: ");
   scanf("%d%d",&x,&y);
   printf("\n y power x is: %f", xy_power());
}

// Definition of function xy_power()

float xy_power(void)
{
   float result  ;
   int a , b ;
   a = x ;
   b = y ;
   result = pow1(b,a) ;
   return(result) ;
}
/* Definition of function  pow1() */

int pow1( int base, register int exponent)
{
   register int t ;
   t = 1;
   for( ; exponent ; exponent--)
   {
     t *= base ;
   }
   return(t);
}
```

Program 17.

```
/****************************************/
/*************   funct_ref.c   ***********/
/****************************************/

# include<stdio.h>

void exchange(float * , float * ) ; /* Prototype */

void main()
{
    float x , y ;
    printf("\n Enter Value for x and y: ");
    scanf("%f%f", &x,&y);
    exchange(&x,&y);
    printf("\n Value of x = %f \n Value of y =
    %f",x,y);
}

// Definition of function

void exchange(float *x , float *y )
{
    float t ;
    t = *x ;    /* copy x into t */
    *x = *y ;   /* copy y into x */
    *y = t ;    /* copy x into y */
}
```

Program 18.

```
/* functovr.c */

#include <stdio.h>
#include <time.h>

float add_em(long int a, float b)
 {
    float result;
    result = a + b;
    return(result);
```

(Contd.)

```
}

void main(void)
 {
   long int i;
   float result = 0;
   time_t start_time, stop_time;
   printf("Working...\n");
   time(&start_time);

   for (i = 1; i <= 100000000L; i++)
      result += i;

   time(&stop_time);

   printf("Using loop:  %d seconds\n", stop_time -
   start_time);

   printf("Working...\n");
   time(&start_time);

   for (i = 1; i <= 100000000L; i++)
   result = add_em(i, result);

   time(&stop_time);

   printf("Using function:  %d seconds\n",
   stop_time - start_time);
 }
```

Program 19.

```
/******************************************/
/**************    main.c    **************/
/******************************************/

# include<stdio.h>

void main(int argc, char *argv[] )
{
   if(argc == 1 )
   {
```

(Contd.)

```
      printf("\nDrastic Change in Environment of
      Computer ");
      printf("\n Program File = %s",argv[0]) ;
    }
    else
    printf("\n Thanking You ");
}
```

Program 20.

```
/****************************************/
/*************** n_fact.c **************/
/****************************************/

# include<stdio.h>

  void main()
    {
       int number ;
       long int factorial ;
       printf("\n Enter Number: ");
       scanf("%d",&number);
       factorial = factorial_of_natural_number
       (number);
       printf("\n Factorial of %d is %ld ",number,
       factorial);
       printf("\n Press a Key ");
       getchar();
    }

    /* Definition of function */

      factorial_of_natural_number(int n )
    {
      int result ;
      if (( n == 1 ) || (n == 0 ))
      return( 1 ) ;
      result = n * factorial_of_natural_number( n
      - 1 );
      return(result);
    }
```

Program 21.

```
// noeffect.c

#include <stdio.h>

void display_and_change(int first, int second, int
third)
{
    printf("Original function parameters values %d
    %d %d\n",
        first, second, third);
        first += 100;
        second += 100;
        third += 100;

    printf("Values after adding 100 to each
    parameter  in function %d, %d, %d\n",
        first, second, third);
}

void main(void)
{
    int x = 100;
    int y = 200;
    int z = 300;

    printf("Values before function call: %d, %d,
    %d\n", x, y, z);
    display_and_change(x, y, z);

    printf("Values after function call: %d, %d,
    %d\n", x, y ,z);
}
```

Program 22.

```
/*******************************************/
/**************  point_f.c  ***************/
/*******************************************/

# include<stdio.h>
```

(Contd.)

```
# include<string.h>

void compare(char * , char * , int(*comp) (char *
char * ) ) ; /* prototype */

void main()
{
    char string1[40],string2[40] ;
    int (*point)() ;

    point = strcmp ; /* get address of strcmp
    function */

    printf("Enter two string: ") ;
    gets(string1) ;
    gets(string2) ;
    compare(string1,string2,point) ;
}

/* Definition of function */

void compare(char *s1, char *s2, int (*comp) (char
* , char * ))
{
    if( !(*comp)(s1,s2))
    {
      printf("\n Strings are  equal ");
      printf("\n Press a Key ");
      getchar() ;
    }

    else
    {
      printf("\n Not equal ");
      printf("\n Press a Key ");
      getchar() ;
    }
}
```

Program 23.

```
/****************************************/
/************** printn.c ***************/
/****************************************/

void printf_number(int number[10], int n )
{
    int i ;
    for( i = 0 ; i < n ; i++ )
      printf("\nIndex = %d \n Number =
      %d",i,number[i]);
}
```

Program 24.

```
/****************************************/
/************** prog10.c ***************/
/****************************************/

# include<stdio.h>

int radix( int ) ; /* Prototype */

void main()
{
    int x ;
    int r ;

    x = 20 ;
    r =  radix(x) ;
    printf(" %d",r);
}

/* Definition of function */

float radix(float n )
{
    int r ;
    r = n % 10 ;
    return(r) ;
}
```

Program 25.

```
// recurs.c

#include <stdio.h>
#include <time.h>

int Length(const char *str)
{
    if (*str)
      return(1 + Length(str+1));
    else
      return(0);
}

void main(void)
{
    long int counter;

    time_t start_time, end_time;

    time(&start_time);
    printf("\n Processing under progress...");
    for (counter = 0; counter < 100000000L;
    counter++)
      Length("No alternative of hard work");

      time(&end_time);

    printf("Processing time = %d seconds\n",
    end_time - start_time);
}
```

Program 26.

```
// rem_recu.c

#include <stdio.h>
#include <time.h>

int Length(const char *str)
{
```

(Contd.)

```
    int length = 0;

    while (*str++)
      length++;

    return(length);
}

void main(void)
{
    long int counter;

    time_t start_time, end_time;

    time(&start_time);
    printf("\n Processing under progress...");
    for (counter = 0; counter < 100000000L;
    counter++)
    Length("No alternative of hard work");

    time(&end_time);

    printf("Processing time = %d seconds\n",
    end_time - start_time);
}
```

Program 27.

```
/****************************************/
/**************  search.c  **************/
/****************************************/

# include<stdio.h>

void main()
{
    int el_to_be_search ;
    int i ;
    int list[100] ;
    for( i = 0 ; i <= 10 ; i++ )
      list [ i ] = i*i ;
    printf("\n List is as follows");
    for( i = 0 ; i <= 10 ; i++ )
```

(Contd.)

```
    printf("\n Index = %d Element = %d", i, list [
    i ]);

    printf("\n Enter Element to be search: ");
    scanf("%d",&el_to_be_search);
    search(list , el_to_be_search, i) ;
}

/* Function definition */
search(int *list , int el_to_be_search, int i)
{
    int j ;
    int l , m , r ;
    int iter = 0 ;
    l = 0 ;
    r = i -1 ;
    do
    {
      iter++ ;
      m = ( l + r ) / 2 ;
      if( el_to_be_search > list[m] )
        l = m + 1 ;
      else
        r = m - 1 ;
    } while((list[m] != el_to_be_search) && ( l <=
      r ));
    if( list[m] == el_to_be_search )
      printf("\n Found = %d \n Position =
      %d",el_to_be_search,m+1 );

    else
      printf("\n Not found and total comparision =
      %d", iter) ;
    return ;
}
```

Program 28.

```
/*****************************************/
/*************   struct.c   **************/
/*****************************************/

# include<stdio.h>
struct record
```

(Contd.)

```
{
    char name[40];
    int age ;
};

void listing( struct record list[10] , int  );

void main()
{
    struct record rec[10] ;
    int i , m ;

    printf("\n Number of record want to read: ");
    scanf("%d",&m);
    printf("\n****************");
    printf("\n List of record ");
    printf("\n****************\n");
    listing( rec, m );  /* invoke listing() */

    for( i = 0; i < m ; i++)
    {
      printf("\n Name: ");
      puts(rec[i].name);
      printf("\nAge: %d\n",rec[i].age);
    }
      printf("\n****************\n");
}

/* Definition of function */

void listing ( struct record list[10] , int n )
{
    struct record rec ;
    int i ;

    for( i = 0 ; i < n ; i++)
    {
      printf(" \n Enter Name: ");
      scanf("%s",rec.name);
      printf("\nEnter age:");
      scanf("\n%d",&rec.age);
      list[i] = rec ;
    }
}
```

Section V

Program 1.

```
/* prog71.c */

# include<stdio.h>
void main()
{
    char value;              /* value is char type */
    char ch = 'A';               /* ch is char type */
    char * address;
        /* pointer variable address is char type */
    address = &ch;
        /*  assign address of ch to pointer variable
            address */
    value = *address;
    printf("\n Address of ch:0x%X", address);
                           /* prints address of ch */
    printf("\n Value of ch: %d", value );
                     /* prints integer value of 'A' */
    printf("\n Value of ch: %c", value);
                             /* prints value of ch */
}
```

Program 2.

```
/* prog710.c */

#include <stdio.h>

void main()
```

(Contd.)

```
{
    double  dub = 200.75;
    double *double_ptr;
                        /* Declare pointer variable */

    double_ptr = &dub:        /* Assign the address*/

    printf("Addres in double_ptr: %x Value at
    *double_ptr: %f \n", double_ptr, *double_ptr);

    *double_ptr = 225.725;
                      /* Change the value in memory */

    printf("Value of dub: %f\n", dub);
}
```

Program 3.

```
/* prog711.c */

# include<stdio.h>

void main()
{
    char p1 = 'H';
    char p2 = 'E';
    char p3 = 'L';
    char p4 = 'L';
    char p5 = 'O';

    char *ptr1 = &p1;
    char *ptr2 = &p2;
    char *ptr3 = &p3;
    char *ptr4 = &p4;
    char *ptr5 = &p5;

    printf("\n %c%c%c%c%c",p1,p2,p3,p4,p5);
    printf("\n
    %c%c%c%c",*ptr1,*ptr2,*ptr3,*ptr4,*ptr5);
}
```

Program 4.

```
/* prog712.c */
# include<stdio.h>
void main()
{
    int x, *sptr, **dptr, ***tptr;
    x = 200;
    sptr = &x;
    dptr = &sptr;
    tptr = &dptr;

    printf("\n Single level pointer indirection:
    address: 0x%X Value: %d",sptr, *sptr);
    printf("\n Two level pointer indirection:
    address: 0x%X Value: %d",dptr, **dptr);
    printf("\n Three level pointer indirection:
    address: 0x%X Value: %d",tptr,***tptr);
}
```

Program 5.

```
/* prog713.c */

#include <stdio.h>

float what_is_the_value(float ***ptr)
{
    return(***ptr);
}

void main(void)
{

    float *level_1, **level_2, ***level_3, value =
    100.125;

    level_1 = &value;
    level_2 = &level_1;
    level_3 = &level_2;
```

(Contd.)

```
    printf("\n Single level: 0x%X", level_1);
    printf("\n Two level: 0x%X", level_2);
    printf("\n Three level: 0x%X", level_3);
    printf("\n The value is: %f \n",
    what_is_the_value(level_3));
}
```

Program 6.

```
/* prog714.c */

#include <stdio.h>

void main()
{
   int values[] = {
   11, 22, 33, 44, 55, 66, 77, 88, 99, 100, 8888
};
   int counter;
   int *iptr;

   iptr = values;
   counter = sizeof(values)/sizeof(values[0]);

   for (; counter; counter--)
   {
     printf("Address: 0x%X and Value: %d\n",iptr,
     *iptr);
     iptr++;
   }
}
```

Program 7.

```
/* prog715.c */

#include <stdio.h>

void main()
{
    char values[] = {
      'H','E','L','L','O'  };
```

(Contd.)

```
    int counter;
    char *char_ptr;
    char_ptr = values;
    counter = sizeof(values)/sizeof(values[0]);

    for (; counter; counter--)
    {
      printf("Address: 0x%X and Value:
      %c\n",char_ptr, *char_ptr);
      char_ptr++;
    }
}
```

Program 8.

```
/* prog716.c */

# include<stdio.h>

/* Access as an array */

void printstring(char str[])
{
    int t;
    for(t=0; str[t] != '\0'; t++);
    {
      printf("%c",str[t]);
    }
}

/* Access as a pointer */

void putstring (char *str)
{
    while(*str)
    {
      putchar(*str++);
    }
}

void main()
{
```

(Contd.)

```
char string[] ="String with the help of
pointer";
char string1[] ="String with the help of
array";
printf("\n Print a string with the help of
pointer\n");
putstring(string);
printf("\n Print a string with the help of
array\n");
printstring(string1);
```

Program 9.

```
/* prog717.c */

# include<stdio.h>

void main()
{
    int man[10] = {
    100,11,22,33,44,55,66,777,888,999 };
    int i;
    printf("\n Result ");

    for( i = 0 ; i < 10 ; i++ )
    {
      printf(" \n %4d", man[i]);
    }
    printf("\n Preass a key");
    getchar() ;
}
```

Prorgram 10.

```
/* prog718.c */

# include<stdio.h>

void main()
{
    int man[10] = {
    100,11,22,33,44,55,66,777,888,999 };
```

(Contd.)

```
    int i;
    printf("\n Result ");

    for( i = 0 ; i < 10 ; i++ )
    {
      printf(" \n %4d", i[man]);
    }
    printf("\n Preass a key");
    getchar() ;
}
```

Program 11.

```
/* prog719.c */

# include<stdio.h>

void main()
{
    int man[10] = {
    100,11,22,33,44,55,66,777,888,999 };
    int i;
    printf("\n Result ");
    for( i = 0 ; i < 10 ; i++ )
    {
      printf("\n %4d",*(man+i));
    }
    printf("\n Preass a key");
    getchar() ;
}
```

Program 12.

```
/* prog72.c */

# include<stdio.h>

void main()
{
    float x;
    int  y;
    char z;
```

(Contd.)

```
    printf("Location of x in memory: 0x%X \n", &x);
    printf("Location of y in memory: 0x%X \n", &y);
    printf("Location of z in memory: 0x%X \n", &z);
}
```

Program 13.

```
/* prog720.c */

# include<stdio.h>

void main()
{
    int man[10] = {
    100,11,22,33,44,55,66,777,888,999 };
    int i;
    printf("\n Result ");

    for( i = 0 ; i < 10 ; i++ )
    {
      printf(" \n 0x%X", &i[man]);
    }
    printf("\n Preass a key");
    getchar() ;
}
```

Program 14.

```
/* prog721.c */

# include<stdio.h>

void main()
{
    int man[10] = {
    100,11,22,33,44,55,66,777,888,999 };
    int i;
    printf("\n Result ");
    for( i = 0 ; i < 10 ; i++ )
    {
      printf("\n %4d", *man++);
    }
```

(Contd.)

```
    printf("\n Preass a key");
    getchar() ;
}
```

Program 15.

```
/* prog722.c */

# include<stdio.h>
# include<string.h>

void main()
{
    char carray[30] = "TOM ALTER LIVES IN
    CALIFORNIA";
    int i ;

    for( i = 0 ; i < strlen(carray); i++)
    {
      printf("%c",carray[i]) ;
    }
}
```

Program 16.

```
/* prog723.c */

# include<stdio.h>
# include<string.h>

void main()
{
    char carray[30] = "TOM ALTER LIVES IN
    CALIFORNIA";
    char *pca ;
    int i ;
    pca = carray ; /* assign the starting
           address of carray  to pca */
    printf("\n Lenght of string =
    %d\n",strlen(carray));
    for( i = 0 ; i < strlen(carray); i++ )
    {
```

(Contd.)

```
        putchar(*(pca));
        pca ++ ; /* increment the pointer */
      }
  }
```

Program 17.

```
/* prog724.c */

# include<stdio.h>

void main()
{
    char carray[] = {
    "TOM ALTER LIVES IN CALIFORNIA"  };
    char *point;
    point = &carray[0];
    while( *point)
    {
      putchar( *point++);
    }
    getchar();
}
```

Program 18.

```
/* prog725.c */

# include<stdio.h>

void main()
{
    char carray[] = "TOM ALTER LIVES IN
    CALIFORNIA";
    char *pca ;

    pca = carray ;  /* assign the starting
                       address of carray  to pca */
    while(*pca)
    {
      putchar( *(pca));
      pca ++ ; /* increment the pointer */
    }
}
```

Program 19.

```
/* prog726.c */

# include<stdio.h>

void main()
{
    char carray[30] = "TOM ALTER LIVES IN
    CALIFORNIA";
    while( *carray )
    {
      putchar( *(carray++));  /* Lvalue required */
    }
}
```

Program 20.

```
/* prog727.c */

# include<stdio.h>

void main()
{
    char carray[] = "TOM ALTER LIVES IN
    CALIFORNIA";
    void *first ;
    first = &carray[0];
    printf("%s",(char *)first);
}
```

Program 21.

```
/* prog728.c */

void output(int *str[])
{
    int i;
    for(i=0; i<3; i++)
      printf("\n %d", str[i]);
}
void main()
```

(Contd.)

```
{
    int intarray[3][3] = {
      {11,22,33},
      {44,55,66},
      {77,88,99} };
    output(intarray);
}
```

Program 22.

```
/* prog729.c */

# include<stdio.h>
void fun( int ) ;   /* prototype */

void main()
{
    int number ;
    printf("\n Enter number (0-3): ");
    scanf("%d", &number);
    fun(number ) ;
    getchar();
}

/* Definition of function */

void fun(int n)
{
    int i ;
    char *message[30] = {
                " Can not open file \n ",
                " Read eoor \n ",
                " Write error \n ",
                " Media failure \n "
              };
    printf("\n %s", message[n]) ;
}
```

Program 23.

```
/* prog73.c */

# include<stdio.h>
void fun();                                   /* prototype */
```

(Contd.)

```
/* Global data type declaration */

float f;
int  i;
char c;

void main()
{
    float f;
    int  i;
    char c;
    f = 40.4 ;
    i = 100 ;
    c = 'c' ;

    printf("\nSTACK ADDRESS\n");
    printf("Location of f in memory: 0x%X \n", &f);
    printf("Location of i in memory: 0x%X \n", &i);
    printf("Location of c in memory: 0x%X \n", &c);
    printf("\nHEAP ADDRESS BECAUSE THE VARIABLES");
    printf("ARE DECLARED AS AN extern  TYPE \n");

    fun(); /* invoke function fun() */
}

/* Definition of function fun() */

void fun()
{
    extern float f;
    extern int  i;
    extern char c;

    printf("Location of f in memory: 0x%X \n", &f);
    printf("Location of i in memory: 0x%X \n", &i);
    printf("Location of c in memory: 0x%X \n", &c);
```

Program 24.

```
/* prog730.c */

# include<stdio.h>
float cube(float a, float *b)
{
    *b = *b * *b * *b ;
    return(a * a * a);
}
void main()
{
    float x = 2.5;
    float y = 5.5;
    printf("\n cube of 2.5 is %f \n", cube(x, &y));
    printf("\n cube of 5.5 is %f", y);
}
```

Program 25.

```
/* prog731.c */

# include<stdio.h>
void cube(float *a, float *b)
{
    *b *= *b * *b;
    *a *= *a * *a;
}
void main()
{
    float x = 2.5;
    float y = 5.5;
    cube(&x, &y);
    printf("\n cube of 2.5 is %f \n", x);
    printf("\n cube of 5.5 is %f", y);
}
```

Program 26.

```
/* prog732.c */

# include<stdio.h>

void cube(float *a, float *b)
{
    *b *= *b * *b;
    *a *= *a * *a;
}
void main()
{
    float x = 2.5;
    float y = 5.5;

    cube(&x, &y);
    printf("\n Address of x is 0x%X",&x);
    printf("\n Address of y is 0x%X \n",&y);

    printf("\n cube of 2.5 is %f \n", x);
    printf("\n cube of 5.5 is %f", y);
}
```

Program 27.

```
/* prog733.c */

# include<stdio.h>
# include<string.h>

int hide(char *c, int (*spider)(char *c))
{
    return((*spider)(c));
}

int length(char *s)
{
    int x = 0;
    while(*s++)
      ++x;
    return(x);
```

(Contd.)

```
}

void main()
{
    int x;
    char *s = "POINTERS";
    x = hide(s, length);
    printf("\n Length of %s is %d",s, x);
}
```

Program 28.

```
/* prog734.c */

# include<stdio.h>

char *combine(char *s, char *t)
{
    int x = 0;
    char str[100];
    while(*s)
    {
      str[x] = *s++;
      x++;
    }
    while(*t)
    {
      str[x] = *t++;
      x++;
    }
    str[x] = '\0';
    return(str);
}

main()
{
    char str[100] = "Butter", str1[100] = "fly",
    *ptr;
    ptr = combine(str, str1);
    printf("\n Combined string is %s", ptr);
}
```

Program 29.

```
/* prog735.c */

/* Pointer and function with array */

# include<stdio.h>

/* Prototype */

void pointer_fun( int *);

void main()
{
    int p[10] = {
    12,13,14,15,16,18,19,234,100,400 };
    int *pointer ;

    pointer = p;  /* assign starting address of
    array p */

    pointer_fun(pointer); /* invoke function */
}

/* Definition of function */

void  pointer_fun(int *ptr)
{
    int i=0;

    while(i<10)
    {
      printf(" value = %d\n", *ptr); /* gives value */
      i++;
      ptr++;
    }
}
```

Program 30.

```
/* prog736.c */

/* pointer and function with string  */

# include<stdio.h>

/* prototype */

void pointer_fun( char *);

void main()
{
    char  p[60] = {
      "NO ALTERNATIVE OF LABOUR"  };
    pointer_fun( p);
    printf("\n Press a key");
    getchar() ;
}

void  pointer_fun(char *p)
{
    while(*p)
    {
      printf(" value = %c\n", *p); /* give value */
      p++;
    }
}
```

Program 31.

```
/* prog737.c */

/* pointer and function with string  */

# include<stdio.h>

/* prototype */

void pointer_fun( char *, char *);
```

(Contd.)

```
void main()
{
    char  p[60] = {
      "NO ALTERNATIVE OF LABOUR " };
    char *cp;
    pointer_fun(p, cp);

    while(*cp)
    {
      printf("%c",*cp++);
    }
}

void  pointer_fun(char *p, char *cp)
{
    while(*p)
    {
      *cp++ = *p++;
    }
    *cp = '\0';
}
```

Program 32.

```
/* prog738.c */

/* pointer string and function   */

# include<stdio.h>

/* prototype */

void pointer_fun( char **);

void main()
{
    char *year_month[] = {
              "JANUARY",
              "FEBUARY",
              "MARCH",
              "APRIL",
              "MAY",
```

(Contd.)

```
                "JUNE" ,
                "AUGUST",
                "SEPTEMBER",
                "OCTOBER",
                "NOVEMBER",
                "DECEMBER"
              };

    pointer_fun(year_month);
    printf("\n Press a key");
    getchar() ;
}

void  pointer_fun(char *p[])
{
    int i=0;

    while(i<11)
    {
      printf(" %s\n", p[i]);
      i++;
    }
}
```

Program 33.

```
/* prog739.c */

/* pointer string and function   */

# include<stdio.h>
# include<string.h>

/* prototype */

void pointer_fun( char **);

void main()
{
    char *year_month[] = {
                "JANUARY",
                "FEBUARY",
```

(Contd.)

```
                "MARCH",
                "APRIL",
                "MAY",
                "JUNE" ,
                "AUGUST",
                "SEPTEMBER",
                "OCTOBER",
                "NOVEMBER",
                "DECEMBER"
              };

    pointer_fun(year_month);
    printf("\n Press a key");
    getchar() ;
}

void  pointer_fun(char *p[])
{
    int i=0;
    int j ;
    while(i<11)
    {
      printf("\n");
      for( j = 0 ; j  < strlen (p[i]) ; j++ )
      {
        printf(" \n %c", p[i][j]);
      }
      printf("\n Press a key");
      getchar() ;
      i++;
    }
}
```

Program 34.

```
/* prog74.c */

# include<stdio.h>

void main()
{
    float x;
```

(Contd.)

```
    int  y;
    char ch;
    int *pointer ;

    x = 200.5 ;
    y = 10 ;
    ch = 'a' ;

    printf("\n STACK ADDRESS\n");

    printf("\n Memory location of x in memory: 0x%X
    \n", &x);
    printf("\n Memory location of y in memory: 0x%X
    \n", &y);
    printf("\n Memory location of ch in memory:
    0x%X \n", &ch);

    pointer = &x ;
    printf("\n Memory location of x in memory: 0x%X
    \n", pointer);

    pointer = &y ;
    printf("\n Memory location of y in memory: 0x%X
    \n", pointer);

    pointer = &ch;
    printf("\n Memory location of ch in memory:
    0x%X \n", &ch);
}
```

Program 35.

```
/* prog740.c */

# include<stdio.h>

struct link
{
    int info ;
    struct link *next ;
};
typedef struct link l;
```

(Contd.)

```
void main()
{
    l *head;
    l *root;
    int i ;
    head = (struct link *)malloc(sizeof(l)) ;
    root=head;
    for( i = 0 ; i < 5 ; i++ )
    {
      head->info = i ;
      head->next = (struct link *)malloc(sizeof(l));
      head=head->next;
    }
    head=root;
    for( i = 0 ; i < 5 ; i++ )
    {
      printf("\n %d",head->info);
      head = head->next ;
      printf("\n Press a key");
      getchar() ;
    }
}
```

Program 36.

```
/* prog741.c */

# include<stdio.h>

void fun() ;  /*  prototype */

struct rec
{
    char name[40];
    char fname[40];
    int age ;
};

void main()
{
    fun() ;
}
```

(Contd.)

```
void fun()
{
    struct rec *record ;
    printf("\n Enter name : ");
    gets(record->name) ;
    printf("\n Enter Fname : ");
    gets(record->fname);
    printf("\nEnter Age : ");
    scanf("%d",&record->age ) ;

    printf("\n Name   : %s",record->name);
    printf("\n FName  : %s",record->fname);
    printf("\n Age    : %d",record->age);
    printf("\n Preass a key");
    getchar() ;
}
```

Program 37.

```
/* prog75.c */

# include<stdio.h>

void main()
{
    float x;
    int  y;
    char ch;
    float *pointer ;
    int *pointer1 ;
    char *pointer2;

    x = 200.5 ;
    y = 10 ;
    ch = 'a' ;

    printf(" \n STACK ADDRESS\n");

    printf(" Location of x in memory: 0x%X\n", &x);
    printf(" Location of y in memory: 0x%X\n", &y);
    printf(" Location of ch in memory: 0x%X\n",
    &ch);
```

(Contd.)

```
    pointer = &x ;
    printf("\n Location of x in memory: 0x%X\n",
    pointer);

    pointer1 = &y ;
    printf(" Location of y in memory: 0x%X\n",
    pointer1);

    pointer2 = &ch;
    printf(" Location of ch in memory: 0x%X\n",
    pointer2);
}
```

Program 38.

```
/* prog76.c */

# include<stdio.h>

void main()
{
    float x;
    int  y;
    char ch;
    float   *pointer ;
    int *pointer1 ;
    char *pointer2;

    x = 200.5 ;
    y = 10 ;
    ch = 'a' ;

    printf(" \n STACK ADDRESS\n");
    printf("\n Location of x in memory: 0x%X \n",
    &x);
    printf("\n Location of y in memory: 0x%X \n",
    &y);
    printf("\n Location of ch in memory: 0x%X \n",
    &ch);

    pointer = &x ;
    printf("\n Value of x: %f \n", *pointer );
```

(Contd.)

```
    pointer1 = &y ;
    printf("\n Value of y: %d \n", *pointer1 );
    pointer2 = &ch;
    printf("\n Value of ch: %c \n", *pointer2 );
}
```

Program 39.

```
/* prog77.c */

# include<stdio.h>

void main()
{
    float a;
    int b;
    float *pa;
    pa = &a;
    *pa = 20.5;

    printf(" \n Value of a %6.3f ", a);
    printf(" \n Value of *pa %6.3f ", *pa);
}
```

Program 40.

```
/* prog78.c */

# include<stdio.h>

void main()
{
    float x;
    int  y;
    char ch;
    void  *pointer ;
    void  *pointer1 ;
    void  *pointer2;

    x = 200.5 ;
    y = 10 ;
    ch = 'a' ;
```

(Contd.)

```
    printf(" \n STACK ADDRESS\n");
    printf("Location of x in memory: 0x%X \n", &x);
    printf("Location of y in memory: 0x%X \n", &y);
    printf("Location of ch in memory: 0x%X \n",
    &ch);

    pointer = &x ;
    printf("Location of x in memory: 0x%X \n",
    pointer);

    pointer1 = &y ;
    printf("Location of y in memory: 0x%X \n",
    pointer1);

    pointer2 = &ch;
    printf("Location of ch in memory: 0x%X \n",
    pointer2);
}
```

Program 41.

```
/* prog79.c */

# include<stdio.h>

void main()
{
    float x;
    int  y;
    char ch;
    void  *pointer ;
    void  *pointer1 ;
    void  *pointer2;

    x = 7200.725 ;
    y = 1110 ;
    ch = 'A' ;

    printf("\n STACK ADDRESS\n");

    printf("\nLocation of x in memory: 0x%X ", &x);
    printf("\nLocation of y in memory: 0x%X ", &y);
```

(Contd.)

```
printf("\nLocation of ch in memory: 0x%X ",
&ch);
pointer = &x ;
printf("\n \n Value of x: %6.4f \n", *(float
*)pointer );

pointer1 = &y ;
printf(" Value of y: %d \n", *(int *)pointer1);

pointer2 = &ch;
printf(" Value of ch: %c \n", *(char *)pointer2 );
```

Section VI

Program 1.

```
gets1(char s[])
{
char ch;
int i =0;
ch = getchar();
while(ch != '\n')
{
s[i] = ch;
i++;
ch = getchar();
}
s[i] = '\0';
}
```

Program 2.

```
/* prog81.c */

# include<stdio.h>
struct Record
{
    char Name[30];
    int AccountNumber;
    double Amount;
};

void main()
{
```

(Contd.)

```
    struct Record Rec;
    printf("\n Input Name: ");
    gets(Rec.Name);
    printf("\n Input Account Number: ");
    scanf("\n %d", &Rec.AccountNumber);
    printf("\n Input Amount:");
    scanf("\n %lf", &Rec.Amount);
    printf("\n Record is as follows");
    printf("\n Name: ");
    puts(Rec.Name);
    printf("\n Account Number:
    %d",Rec.AccountNumber);
    printf("\n Amount: %lf", Rec.Amount);
}
```

Program 3.

```
/* prog810.c */

# include<stdio.h>
# include<malloc.h>

struct Address
{
    char Name[40];
    char Addr[140];
    long int Zip;
};
void Update (struct Address *Ref)
{
    struct Address Reference= {
      "Rachita", "4-C/3 Staff Colony, G.B.P.E.C.
      Campus, Pauri", 246001};
    *Ref = Reference;
}
void main()
{
    struct Address Add;
    Update (&Add);
    puts(Add.Name);
    puts(Add.Addr);
    printf("\n Pin Code: %ld", Add.Zip);
}
```

Program 4.

```
/* prog811.c */

# include<stdio.h>

struct Mailing
{
    char Name[40];
    char Father[40];
    int Age;
    float Salary;
};

struct Mailing Record1 =
{
     "TOM ALTER","WANTE WALTER", 32, 48000.75};

struct Mailing Record2 =

{
     "JORG COOK", "MORTIN COOK", 50, 32000.25};

void main()
{

    struct Mailing *ptr1, *ptr2;
    ptr1 - &Record1;
    ptr2 = &Record2;

    printf("\n Detail of record 1 is as follows
    \n");
    printf("\n Name: ");
    puts(Record1.Name);
    printf(" Father: ");
    puts(Record1.Father);
    printf(" Age: %d", Record1.Age);
    printf("\n Salary: %f", Record1.Salary);
    printf("\n");

    printf("\n Detail of record 1 with the help of
    pointer is as follows \n");
```

(Contd.)

```
    printf("\n Name: ");
    puts((*ptr1).Name);
    printf(" Father: ");
    puts((*ptr1).Father);
    printf(" Age: %d", (*ptr1).Age);
    printf("\n Salary: %f", (*ptr1).Salary);
    printf("\n");
    printf("\n Detail of record 2 is as follows
    \n");
    printf("\n Name: ");
    puts(Record2.Name);
    printf(" Father: ");
    puts(Record2.Father);
    printf(" Age: %d", Record2.Age);
    printf("\n Salary: %f", Record2.Salary);
    printf("\n");
    printf("\n Detail of record 2 with the help of
    pointer is as follows \n");
    printf("\n Name: ");
    puts((*ptr2).Name);
    printf(" Father: ");
    puts((*ptr2).Father);
    printf(" Age: %d", (*ptr2).Age);
    printf("\n Salary: %f", (*ptr2).Salary);
    printf("\n");

/**********************************************/
/******* Different pointer operation *********/
/**********************************************/

    printf("\n Output through different pointer
    operation \n");

    puts((*ptr1).Name);
    puts(ptr1->Name);
    printf(" %d",Record1.Age);
    printf("\n %d",(*ptr1).Age);
    printf("\n %d", ptr1->Age);

    printf("\n Byte level operation \n");

    printf("\n %c", Record1.Name[2]);
    printf("\n %c", (Record1.Name)[2]);
```

(Contd.)

```
    printf("\n %s", ptr1->Name+2);
    printf("\n %s", (ptr1->Name)+2);

    printf("\n %c", *(ptr1->Name+2));
    printf("\n %c", ptr1->Name[2]);
    printf("\n %c", (ptr1->Name)[2]);

    printf("\n %c", *Record2.Name);
    printf("\n %c", *ptr2->Name);
    printf("\n %c", *(ptr2->Name));

    printf("\n %c", Record2.Name);
    printf("\n %c", *(Record2.Name));

    printf("\n %c", *Record2.Name+1);
    printf("\n %c", *ptr2->Name+1);
    printf("\n %c", *(ptr2->Name)+1);
}
```

Program 5.

```
/* prog812.c */

# include<stdio.h>

struct Info
{
    char Name[40];
    char Street[120];
    char Dist[40];
    char State[40];
    long int Pin_code;
};

void main()
{
    struct Info Play ={
    "Tom Alter", "IV-C-III, G.B.P.E.C Campus",
    "Pauri","Uttar Pradesh",246001 };
    FILE *fp ;
    fp = fopen("rec.dat","w");
    if(fp == NULL)
```

(Contd.)

```
    {
      perror("ERROR");
      exit(0);
    }
    fwrite(&Play, sizeof(Play), 1, fp);
    printf("\n Record is as follows \n\n");
    puts(Play.Name);
    puts(Play.Street);
    printf("%s",Play.Dist);
    printf("\n%s",Play.State);
    printf("\n%ld",Play.Pin_code);
    printf("\nPress a key ");
    getchar() ;
}
```

Program 6.

```
/* prog813.c */

# include<stdio.h>

struct Info
{
    char Name[40];
    char Street[120];
    char Dist[40];
    char State[40];
    long int Pin_code;
};

void main()
{
    struct Info Play ={
    "Tom Alter", "IV-C-III, G.B.P.E.C Campus",
    "Pauri","Uttar Pradesh",246001 };
    FILE *fp ;
    fp = fopen("rec.dat","rb+");
    if(fp == NULL)
    {
      perror("ERROR");
      exit(0);
    }
    fwrite(&Play, sizeof(Play), 1, fp);
```

(Contd.)

```
    printf("\n Record is as follows \n\n");
    puts(Play.Name);
    puts(Play.Street);
    printf("%s",Play.Dist);
    printf("\n%s",Play.State);
    printf("\n%ld",Play.Pin_code);
    printf("\nPress a key ");
    getchar() ;
}
```

Program 7.

```
/* prog814.c */

# include<stdio.h>

union demo
{
    char ch;
    int i_num;
    float f_num;
};

void main()
{
    union demo info;
    info.ch = 'A';
    info.i_num = 1234;
    info.f_num = 345.23;

    printf("\n0x %x <= address of ch \n",
    &info.ch);
    printf("\n0x %x <= address of i_num \n",
    &info.i_num);
    printf("\n0x %x <= address of f_num \n",
    &info.f_num);

    printf(" \n Output result ");

    printf("\n %c <= value of ch \n", info.ch);
    printf("\n %d <= value of i_num \n",
info.i_num);
```

(Contd.)

```
    printf("\n %f <= value of f_num \n",
info.f_num);
    printf("\n  Press a key");
    getchar();
}
```

Program 8.

```
/* prog815.c */

# include<stdio.h>

union data
{
    char name[30];
    int age ;
    float salary ;
};

void main()
{
    union data d;
    union data *d1;

    d.age = 30 ;
    d.salary = 7500;
    d1 =  &d;  /* assign address of the d to d1 */
    printf("\n%d",d1->age);
    printf("\n%f",d1->salary);
    printf("\n  Press a key");
    getchar() ;
}
```

Program 9.

```
/* prog816.c */

# include<stdio.h>

struct MailingAddress
{
    char Name[40]; /* First member */
```

(Contd.)

```
    char Father_Name[40]; /* Seond member */
    char City[40]; /* Third member */
    long int Zip; /* Fourth member */
}  Address;

void pass_struct(char str[]);

void main()
{
    struct MailingAddress Address1 = {
    "Tom Alter", "Tom Cook", "California", 93561 };

    pass_struct(Address1.Name);
    pass_struct(Address1.Father_Name);
    pass_struct(&Address1.Name[0]);
    pass_struct(&Address1.Father_Name[0]);
}

void pass_struct(char str[])
{
    puts(str);
}
```

Program 10.

```
/* prog817.c */

# include<stdio.h>

struct Tag_Name
{
    int a;
    char b;
    float f;
};

void fun (struct Tag_Name Ref)
{
    printf("\n Value of a is %d", Ref.a);
    printf("\n Value of b is %c", Ref.b);
    printf("\n Value of f is %f", Ref.f);
}
```

(Contd.)

```
void main()
{
    struct Tag_Name Act;
    Act.a = 200;
    Act.b = 'C';
    Act.f = 875.75;
    fun (Act);
}
```

Program 11.

```
/* prog818.c */

# include<stdio.h>

struct Tag_Name
{
    int a;
    char b;
    float f
};

struct Tag_Name1
{
    int a;
    char b;
    float f;
};

void fun (struct Tag_Name1 Ref)
{
    printf("\n Value of a is %d", Ref.a);
    printf("\n Value of b is %c", Ref.b);
    printf("\n Value of f is %f", Ref.f);
}

void main()
{
    struct Tag_Name Act;

    Act.a = 200;
```

(Contd.)

```
    Act.b = 'C';
    Act.f = 875.75;
    fun (Act);
}
```

Program 12.

```
/* prog82.c */

# include<stdio.h>

struct Address
{
    char Name[30];
    char Street[60];
    char City[100];
    char State[20];
    unsigned long int Pin;
}   Address1;

void main()
{
    printf("\n Input Name: ");
    gets(Address1.Name);
    printf("\n Input Street: ");
    gets(Address1.Street);
    printf("\n Input City: ");
    gets(Address1.City);
    printf("\n Input State: ");
    gets(Address1.State);
    printf("\n Input ZIP: ");
    scanf("\n %ld", &Address1.Pin);

    printf("\n Name: %s", Address1.Name);
    printf("\n Street: %s", Address1.Street);
    printf("\n City: %s", Address1.City);
    printf("\n State: %s", Address1.State);
    printf("\n ZIP: %ld", Address1.Pin);
}
```

Program 13.

```
/* prog83.c */

# include<stdio.h>
struct Address
{
    char Name[30];
    char Street[60];
    char City[100];
    char State[20];
    unsigned long int Pin;
};

void main()
{

    struct Address Address1 =

    {
        "MMS Rauthan",
        "240 Dong Srinagar",
        "Pauri-Garhwal",
        "Uttar Pradesh",
        246010
    };
    struct Address Address2 =
    {
        "Ram Bahaduri Patel",
        "4-C/3 College Campus",
        "G.B.Pant Engg. College, Pauri-Garhwal",
        "Uttar Pradesh",
        246001
    };
    struct Address Address3 =
    {
        "Misthi Rauthan",
        "240 Dong Srinagar",
        "Pauri-Garhwal",
        "Uttar Pradesh",
        246010 };
```

(Contd.)

```
    printf("\n Name: %s", Address1.Name);
    printf("\n Street: %s", Address1.Street);
    printf("\n City: %s", Address1.City);
    printf("\n State: %s", Address1.State);
    printf("\n ZIP: %ld", Address1.Pin);

    printf("\n Name: %s", Address2.Name);
    printf("\n Street: %s", Address2.Street);
    printf("\n City: %s", Address2.City);
    printf("\n State: %s", Address2.State);
    printf("\n ZIP: %ld", Address2.Pin);

    printf("\n Name: %s", Address3.Name);
    printf("\n Street: %s", Address3.Street);
    printf("\n City: %s", Address3.City);
    printf("\n State: %s", Address3.State);
    printf("\n ZIP: %ld", Address3.Pin);
}
```

Program 14.

```
/* prog84.c */

# include<stdio.h>
struct Address
{
    char Name[30];
    char Street[60];
    char City[100];
    char State[20];
    unsigned long int Pin;
}   Address1 =

{
        "MMS Rauthan",
         "240 Dong Srinagar",
         "Pauri-Garhwal",
         "Uttar Pradesh",
         246010
};

void main()
```

(Contd.)

```
{
    printf("\n Name: %s", Address1.Name);
    printf("\n Street: %s", Address1.Street);
    printf("\n City: %s", Address1.City);
    printf("\n State: %s", Address1.State);
    printf("\n ZIP: %ld", Address1.Pin);
}
```

Program 15.

```
/* prog85.c */

# include<stdio.h>

struct Payment
{
    char Name_of_Item [40] ;
    float Cost_of_Item ;
    char Code_of_Item[20];
    int Number_of_Item ;
};

struct Payment Bill1 = {
    "LASER",23500.75,"S/124/1999",10};
struct Payment Bill2 ;

void main()
{
    double Total_cost ;

    Total_cost = Bill1.Number_of_Item *
    Bill1.Cost_of_Item;

    printf("\n Detail of item sold ");
    printf("\n*********************************");
    printf("\n Item code     :
    %s",Bill1.Code_of_Item );
    printf("\n Name of item :
    %s",Bill1.Name_of_Item);
    printf("\n No.of Item      :
    %d",Bill1.Number_of_Item);
    printf("\n Cost of item : %f",
Bill1.Cost_of_Item);
```

(Contd.)

```
    printf("\n Total Cost   : %f",Total_cost ).
    printf("\n*******************************");
    printf("\n  Press A Key ");
    getchar() ;
    Bill2 = Bill1 ;
    printf("\n Detail of item sold ");
    printf("\n*******************************");
    printf("\n Item code    :
    %s",Bill2.Code_of_Item );
    printf("\n Name of item :
    %s",Bill2.Name_of_Item);
    printf("\n No.of Item     :
    %d",Bill2.Number_of_Item);
    printf("\n Cost of item : %f",
    Bill2.Cost_of_Item);
    printf("\n Total Cost   : %f",Total_cost );
    printf("\n*******************************");
    printf("\n  Press A Key ");
    getchar() ;
}
```

Program 16.

```
/* prog86.c */

# include<stdio.h>

struct Person_Name
{
    char First[20];
    char Middle[20];
    char Last[20];
};

struct Student
{
    struct Person_Name Name;
    char SSN[10];
    int Age;
    char Bdate[10];
    char Sex;
}Student1, Student2;
```

(Contd.)

```
void main()
{
   /*  Input section  */

   printf("\n Enter First name: ");
   gets(Student1.Name.First);

   printf("\n Enter Middle name: ");
   gets(Student1.Name.Middle);

   printf("\n Enter Last name: ");
   gets(Student1.Name.Last);

   printf("\nEnter Social Security Number: ");
   gets(Student1.SSN);

   printf("\nEnter Birth date: ");
   gets(Student1.Bdate);
   printf("\n Enter Age: ");
   scanf("%d", &Student1.Age);
   printf("\n Enter Sex: ");
   scanf("%c", Student1.Sex);


   printf("\nREPORT GEGERATION ");
   printf("\n******************");

   printf("\n First name: ");
   puts(Student1.Name.First);

   printf("\n Middle name: ");
   puts(Student1.Name.Middle);

   printf("\n Last name: ");
   puts(Student1.Name.Last);

   printf("\n Social Security Number: ");
   puts(Student1.SSN);

   printf("\n Birth date: ");
   puts(Student1.Bdate);
   printf("\n Age: ");
```

(Contd.)

```
    printf("%d", Student1.Age);
    printf("\n Sex: ");
    printf("%c", Student1.Sex);

}
```

Program 17.

```
/* prog87.c */

/*    Two complex numbers addition    */

# include<stdio.h>
struct complex1
{
    float x ;
    float y ;
};

struct two_complex
{
    struct complex1 comp1 ;
    struct complex1 comp2 ;
};

void main()
{
    struct complex1 comp ;
    struct two_complex new_two_complex = {
                {2.5,4.5},
                {3.5,6.5}  };
    printf("\nFirst Complex Number");
    printf("\n*******************");

    printf("\n%4.1f +
    j4.1%f",new_two_complex.comp1.x,
       new_two_complex.comp1.y);

    printf("\n\n\nSecond Complex Number");
    printf("\n*********************");
    printf("\n%4.1f +
    j%4.1f",new_two_complex.comp2.x,
```

(Contd.)

```
        new_two_complex.comp2.y);

    comp.x = new_two_complex.comp2.x +
    new_two_complex.comp1.x ;
    comp.y = new_two_complex.comp1.y +
    new_two_complex.comp2.y;

    printf("\n\n\n\nSummation of two complex number ");
    printf("\n********************************");
    printf("\n%4.1f + j%4.1f",comp.x,comp.y);
    printf("\n********************************");
    printf("\n Press A Key ");
    getchar() ;
}
```

Program 18.

```
/* prog88.c */

/* Complex number subtraction */

# include<stdio.h>

struct complex1
{
    float x ;
    float y ;
};

struct complex2
{
    struct complex1 comp1 ;
    struct complex1 comp2 ;
};
void main()
{
    struct complex2 cp = {
    10,20,30,40 };
    struct complex2 complex;
    printf("\n Complex Number ");
    printf("\n **************");
```

(Contd.)

```
    printf("\n%4.1f + %4.1fj",cp.comp1.x,
    cp.comp1.y);
    printf("\n%4.1f + %4.1fj",cp.comp2.x ,
    cp.comp2.y);
    printf("\n  Press A Key ");
    getchar() ;

    complex.comp1.x = cp.comp1.x - cp.comp2.x;
    complex.comp1.y = cp.comp1.y - cp.comp2.y;
    printf("\n %4.1f + %4.1jf", complex.comp1.x,
    complex.comp1.y);
}
```

Program 19.

```
/* prog89.c */

# include<stdio.h>

void gets1(char s[]);

struct Emp
{
    char Name [40] ;
    char Dept [120];
    char Status ;
    int Basic_salary ;
    char Address [120];
};

struct Emp Rec [100];

void main()
{
    int no_of_record ;
    int i ;
    printf("\n Enter number of record want to
    process: ");
    scanf("%d",&no_of_record);

    /* Input section */
```

(Contd.)

```
    for( i = 0 ; i < no_of_record ; i++ )
    {
      printf("\n Record number: %d",i+1);
      printf("\nEnter employee name: ");
      gets1(Rec[i].Name);
      printf("\nEnter Deptt: ");
      gets1(Rec[i].Dept);
      printf("\nEnter class: ");
      Rec[i].Status = getchar();
      printf("\n Enter basic salary: ");
      scanf("%d",&Rec[i].Basic_salary);
      printf("\nEnter address of employee: ");
      gets1(Rec[i].Address);
    }

    for( i = 0 ; i < no_of_record ; i++ )
    {
      printf("\n Record Number: %d",i+1);
      printf("\n Employee Name: ");
      puts(Rec[i].Name);
      printf("\n Deptt: ");
      puts(Rec[i].Dept);
      printf("\n Class: ");
      printf("%c",Rec[i].Status);
      printf("\n Basic salary: ");
      printf("%d",Rec[i].Basic_salary);
      printf("\n Address: ");
      puts(Rec[i] Address);
      printf("\n Press a key ");
      getchar() ;
    }

}

void gets1(char s[])
{
char ch;
int i =0;
ch = getchar();
while(ch != '\n')
{
s[i] = ch;
```

(Contd.)

```
i++;
ch = getchar();
}
s[i] = '\0';
}
```

Program 20.

```
/* showequp.c */

#include <stdio.h>
#include <bios.h>

void main(void)
 {
   struct Equip {
          unsigned floppy_available:1;
          unsigned coprocessor_available:1;
          unsigned system_memory:2;
          unsigned video_memory:2;
          unsigned floppy_disk_count:2;
          unsigned unused_1:1;
          unsigned serial_port_count:3;
          unsigned game_adapter_available:1;
          unsigned unused_2:1;
          unsigned printer_count:2;
};

   union Equipment {
          unsigned list;
          struct Equip list_bits;
         } equip;

   equip.list = _bios_equiplist();

       if (equip.list_bits.coprocessor_available)
          printf("Math coprocessor available\n");
       else
          printf("No math coprocessor\n");

       printf("System board memory %d\n",
          (equip.list_bits.system_memory + 1) * 16);
```

(Contd.)

```
printf("Number of floppies %d\n",
    equip.list_bits.floppy_disk_count + 1);

printf("Number of printers %d\n",
    equip.list_bits.printer_count);

printf("Number of serial ports %d\n",
    equip.list_bits.serial_port_count);
```

Section VII

Program 1.

```
/* access.c */

/* This program segment checks access permission of
the file */

#include <stdio.h>
#include <unistd.h>

void main (int argc, char *argv[])
{
    int access_mode;
    int i;
    for(i =0; i< argc; i++)
    {
      access_mode = access(argv[i], 0);

      if (access_mode)
        printf("File %s does not exist\n", argv[i]);
      else
      {
        access_mode = access(argv[i], 2);

        if (access_mode)
          printf("File %s cannot be written\n",
          argv[i]);
        else
          printf("File %s can be written\n",
          argv[i]);
```

(Contd.)

```
      access_mode = access(argv[i], 4);

      if (access_mode)
        printf("File %s cannot be read\n",
        argv[i]);
      else
        printf("File %s can be read\n", argv[i]);

      access_mode = access(argv[i], 6);

      if (access_mode)
        printf("File %s cannot be read/write\n",
        argv[i]);
      else
        printf("File %s can be read/write\n",
        argv[i]);
    }
  }
}
```

Program 2.

```
/* chdir.c */

# include <stdio.h>
# include <stdlib.h>
# include <errno.h>
# include<limits.h>

void main (int argc, char *argv[])
{
    char directory[_POSIX_PATH_MAX];

    if (argc == 1)
               /* Display the current directory */
    {
      getcwd(directory, _POSIX_PATH_MAX);
      puts(directory);
    }
    else if ((chdir(argv[1])) && (errno == ENOENT))
      puts("Invalid directory");
}
```

Program 3.

```
/* chmod.c */

#include <stdio.h>
#include <sys/stat.h>

void main(int argc, char *argv[])
{
    if (chmod(argv[1], S_IREAD))
                    /* set flag in read mode only */
    {   /* if one want set in write set the flag */
        /* S_IWRITE */
        /* if we interested in read/write then set
            the flag S_IWRITE|S_IREAD */

      printf("Error setting %s\n", argv[1]);
      perror("Error:");
      exit(1);
    }
}
```

Program 4.

```
/* creatdir.c */

# include<stdio.h>
# include<sys/types.h>
# include<sys/stat.h>

void main(int argc, char *argv[])
{
    if(argc != 2)
    {
      printf("\n File parameters not provided
      properly ");
      perror("\n Error: ");
      exit(1);
    }

    if(mkdir(argv[1], 0777) == -1)
    {
```

(Contd.)

```
        printf("\n %s directory not created \n ",
        argv[1]);
        perror("Error: ");
        exit(2);
      }
      if(chdir(argv[1]) == -1)
        printf("\n Directory %s not changed ",
        argv[1]);
}
```

Program 5.

```
/* ferror.c */

#include <stdio.h>
#include <stdlib.h>

void main (int argc, char *argv[])
{
    FILE *fp;

    char line[256];

    if (fp = fopen(argv[1], "r"))
    {
      while (fgets(line, sizeof(line), fp))
      {
        if (ferror(fp))
        {
          fprintf(stderr, "Error reading from %s\n",
          argv[1]);
          exit(1);
        }
        else
        {
          fputs(line, stdout);
          if (ferror(fp))
          {
            fprintf(stderr, "Error writing to
            stdout\n");
            exit(1);
          }
```

(Contd.)

```
        }
      }
    }
    else
      printf("Error opening %s\n", argv[1]);
}
```

Program 6.

```
/* fileno.c */

#include <stdio.h>

void main (int argc, char *argv[])
{
    FILE *stream1, *stream2;
    int handle1, handle2;
    int size = 128;
    char buffer[128];

    if (stream1 = fopen(argv[1], "r"))
      if (stream2 = fopen(argv[2], "w"))
      {
          /* Finding handle of opened file argv[1]
             and argv[2] */

        handle1 = fileno(stream1);
        handle2 = fileno(stream2);

        read(handle1, buffer, size);
        write(handle2, buffer, size);

        fclose(stream1);
        fclose(stream2);
      }
      else
        printf("Error opening %s\n", argv[2]);
    else
      printf("Error opening %s\n", argv[1]);
```

Program 7.

```
    /* filesize.c */

# include<stdio.h>
# include<stdlib.h>

void main(int argc, char *argv[])
{
    FILE *fp;
    int count = 0;
    if (argc != 2)
    {
      printf("\n Proper number of arguments are not
      supplied");
      exit(1);
    }
    fp = fopen (argv[1], "r");
    if(fp == NULL)
    {
      printf ("\n Can not open file %s", argv[1]);
      perror("Error: ");
      exit(1);
    }
    while(getc(fp) != EOF)
      count++;
    fclose(fp);
    printf("\n %s contains %d", argv[1], count);
}
```

Program 8.

```
/* filesstat.c */

# include<stdio.h>
# include<sys/types.h>
# include<sys/stat.h>

/* Prototypes */

int show_stat( struct stat *);
int show_access(unsigned short);
```

(Contd.)

```
void main(int argc, char *argv[])
{
    struct stat status;
    int i;
    for(i = 0; i <argc; i++)
    {
      if (stat(argv[i], &status)== -1)
      {
        printf("\n No status information for %s",
        argv[i]);
      }
      else
      {
        printf("\n Status information for %s",
        argv[i]);
        show_stat(&status);
      }
    }
}

/* Function show_stat() display the information
associated with a file */

int show_stat(struct stat *info)
{
    printf("\n File type: ");
    switch(info->st_mode&S_IFMT)
    {
    case S_IFDIR:
      printf("\n Directory ");
      break;
    case S_IFREG:
      printf("\n Normal file ");
      break;
    case S_IFCHR:
      printf("\n Character device ");
      break;
    case S_IFBLK:
      printf("\n Block  device ");
      break;
    case S_IFIFO:
      printf("\n FIFO");
      break;
    }
```

(Contd.)

```
    printf("\n i-node number: %d", info->st_ino);
    printf("\n Access permission for User: ");
    show_access(info->st_mode>>6);
    printf("\n Access permission for Group: ");
    show_access(info->st_mode>>3);
    printf("\n Number of references %d",info-
    >st_nlink);
    printf("\n User number: %d ", info->st_uid);
    printf("\n Group number: %d ", info->st_gid);
    printf("\n File size: %ld bytes", info-
    >st_size);
    printf("\n Last access: %s", ctime(&(info-
    >st_atime)));

    printf("\n Last editing: %s ", ctime (&(info-
    >st_mtime)));
    printf("\n Last status change: %s ", ctime
    (&(info->st_ctime)));
}
/* Show the access permission */
/* function show_access() */

int show_access(unsigned short mode)
{
    if(mode & 04)
      printf("\n Read");
    if(mode & 02)
      printf("\n Write ");
    if(mode & 01)
      printf("\n Execute ");
}
```

Program 9.

```
/* format.c */

# include<stdio.h>
# include<stdlib.h>

void main()
{
    FILE *fp;
```

(Contd.)

```
    int ivalue = 125;
    float fvalue = 125.125;
    char string [20] = "Enjoy with C";

    fp = fopen("form.dat", "w");
    if (fp == NULL)
    {
      printf("\n File TEST can not be created \n");
      perror("Error: ");
      exit(1);
    }

    printf("\nInteger value: %0d \n Hexdecimal
    value: %x \n", ivalue, ivalue);
    printf("\n Integer value: %6d\n", ivalue);
    printf("\nOctal value: %o \n General value:
    %#o\n" , ivalue, ivalue);
    printf("\n %f, \n %9.4f \n %*.*f \n %E \n",
    fvalue, fvalue,8, 1, fvalue, fvalue);
    printf("\n %s \n %20s \n %-20s \n %c \n",
    string, string, string, string);

    fprintf(fp,"\nInteger value: %0d \n Hexdecimal
    value: %x \n", ivalue, ivalue);
    fprintf(fp,"\n Integer value: %6d\n", ivalue);
    fprintf(fp,"\nOctal value: %o \n General value:
    %#o\n" , ivalue, ivalue);
    fprintf(fp,"\n %f, \n %9.4f \n %*.*f \n %E \n",
    fvalue, fvalue, 8, 1, fvalue, fvalue);
    fprintf(fp, "\n %s \n %20s \n %-20s \n %c \n",
    string, string, string, string);
fclose(fp);
}
```

Program 10.

```
/* fprintf.c */

#include <stdio.h>
void main (void)
{
```

(Contd.)

```
    FILE *fp;

    int pages = 695;
    float price = 250.0;
    if (fp = fopen("FPRINTF.DAT", "w"))
    {
      fprintf(fp, "Book Title: Expert Data
      Structures With C++ \n");
      fprintf(fp, "Pages: %d\n", pages);
      fprintf(fp, "Price: $%6.25f\n", price);
      fclose(fp);
    }
    else
      printf("Error opening FPRINTF.DAT\n");
}
```

Program 11.

```
/* freopen.c */

# include<stdio.h>
# include<stdlib.h>

void main()
{
    int ch;
    FILE *fp;

    if((fp = freopen ("freopen.dat", "w", stdout))
    == (FILE *) NULL)
    {
      printf("\n File FDOPEN.DAT open error");
      perror("Error: ");
      exit(1);
    }
    while(( ch = getchar()) != '\n')
    {
      putchar(ch);
    }
}
```

Program 12.

```
/* fscanf.c */

#include <stdio.h>

void main(void)
{
    FILE *fp;

    int age;
    float salary;
    char name[64];

    if ((fp = fopen("DATA.DAT", "w")) == NULL)
      printf("Error opening DATA.DAT for output\n");
    else
    {
      fprintf(fp, "21 11125.7535 Rachita");
      fclose(fp);

      if ((fp = fopen("DATA.DAT", "r")) == NULL)
        printf("Error opening DATA.DAT for
        input\n");
      else
      {
        fscanf(fp, "%d %f %s", &age, &salary, name);
        printf("\n Age: %d \n Salary: %f \n Name:
        %s\n", age, salary, name);
        fclose(fp);
      }
    }
}
```

Program 13.

```
/* ftell.c */

#include <stdio.h>
# include<stdlib.h>

void main(void)
{
```

(Contd.)

```
    FILE *input;

    int letter;

    if ((input = fopen("dest", "r")) == NULL)
      printf("Error opening DEST \n");
    else
    {
      printf("Current position is byte %d\n\n",
      ftell(input));

/*  Read and write each character in the file */
      /* standard output device */

      while ((letter = fgetc(input)) != EOF)
      {
        fputc(letter, stdout);

        printf("\nCurrent position is byte %d\n",
        ftell(input));
      }
      fclose(input);    /* Close the input file */
    }
}
```

Program 14.

```
/* mount.c */

# include<stdio.h>
# include<sys/mount.h>
# include<limits.h>

void main()
{
    char direc[_POSIX_PATH_MAX];
    char device[_POSIX_PATH_MAX];

    printf("\n Mounting a file system: \n");

    printf("\n Directory: > ");
    scanf("%s", direc);
```

(Contd.)

```
    if(mount(device, direc, 0) == -1)
      printf("\n Error during mounting: \n");
    else
      printf("\n <%s> mounted in the directory <%s>
      \n ", device, direc);
}
```

Program 15.

```
/* newtime.c */

# include<stdio.h>
# include<utime.h>
# include<sys/stat.h>
# include<sys/types.h>

struct utimebuf
{
    time_t actime ; /* last read time */
    time_t modtime; /* last edinting time */
};

void main(int argc, char *argv[])
{
    struct stat status;
                        /* file status information */
    struct utimebuf ftime; /* new access time */
    while(--argc)
    {
      printf("\n %s \n ", argv[argc]);
      if(stat(argv[argc], &status) == -1 )
        printf("\n No status for the file %s",
        argv[argc]);
      else
      {
        printf("\n Last read for the file: %s : %s",
        argv[argc], ctime(&(status.st_atime)));
        printf("\n Last editing for the file: %s :
        %s",argv[argc], ctime(&(status.st_mtime)));
```

(Contd.)

```
        if(status.st_atime>status.st_mtime)
          ftime.actime = ftime.modtime=
                              status.st_atime;
        else
          ftime.actime = ftime.modtime
                            = status.st_atime;
        if(utime(argv[argc], &ftime) == -1)
          printf("\n %s not edited \n", argv[argc]);
        else
          printf("\n New time: %s",
          ctime(&(ftime.actime)));
      }
    }
}
```

Program 16.

```
/* prog91.c */

# include<stdio.h>

void main()
{
    char ch ;
    FILE *fp ;
    fp = fopen ("test","w");
    if ( fp == NULL )
    {
      perror("ERROR");
      exit(1);
    }
    ch = getchar() ;
    while(ch != '\n' )
    {
      putc(ch,fp);
      ch = getchar();
    }
    fclose(fp);
}
```

Program 17.

```
/* prog910.c */

# include<stdio.h>
# include<string.h>
# include<stdlib.h>

void main()
{
    char file[13];
    int count = 0 ;
    char ch ;
    char name[40];
    char father_name[40];
    char roll_number[8];
    char branch[20];
    int age ;

    FILE *fp;

    printf("\n Enter Database File: ");
    scanf("%s",file);

    fp = fopen(file,"r");
    if( fp == NULL )
    {
      printf("\nFile %s\n",file);
      perror("Error: ");
      exit(1);
    }
    printf("\n Enter choice (y/n): ");
    ch = getchar();
    ch = toupper(ch);

    /* Read section */

label1:
    while(ch == 'Y')
    {
      fscanf(fp,"\n %d",&count);
```

(Contd.)

```
    /* use fgets() function for satisfaction */
    /* or fscanf(fp,"[\^]",name)  this  type */
    /* read operation required with   string */
    /*            type data only             */
    fscanf(fp, "%d", &count);
    fgets(name, 40, fp);
    fscanf(fp, "\n ");
    fgets(father_name, 40, fp);
    fscanf(fp,"\n ");
    fgets(roll_number, 8, fp );
    fscanf(fp,"\n ");
    fgets(branch, 20, fp);
    fscanf(fp,"\n %d",&age);

    /* Output section */

    printf("\n %d",count);
    puts(name);
    puts(father_name);
    puts(roll_number);
    puts(branch);
    printf("\n %d",age);

    printf("\n Enter choice (y/n): ");
    ch = getchar();
    ch = toupper(ch);
  }
  printf("\n Once again want to dislpaly data (y/
  n): ");
  ch = getchar ();
  ch = toupper(ch);
  if(ch == 'Y')
  {
    rewind(fp) ;

    /* return the file pointer to begging of file
if you want to see next dataremove rewind()
function then you will get next record if exists in
the file */

    goto label1 ;
  }
```

(Contd.)

```
    else
    {
      printf("\n Thanking You ");
    }
    fclose(fp);
    printf(" Successfully work on file is done  ");
}
```

Program 18.

```
/* prog911.c */

# include<stdio.h>

struct Address
{
    char Name[40];
    char Street[120];

    char    City[20];
    long int Zip;
    char Country[20];
};

void main()
{
    struct Address per ;
    char file[13];
    FILE *fp;

    printf("\nEnter Database file: ");
    scanf("%s",file);
    fp = fopen (file,"rb+");

    if(fp == NULL)
    {
      printf("\n File %s",file);
      perror("Error");
      exit(1);
    }

    fread(&per, sizeof(per) , 1, fp);
```

(Contd.)

```
    while(!feof(fp))
    {
      puts(per.Name);
      puts(per.Street);
      puts(per.City);
      puts(per.Country);
      printf("%ld",per.Zip);

      fread(&per, sizeof(per) , 1, fp);
      printf("\n Press a key ");
      getchar();
    }
}
```

Program 19.

```
/* prog912.c */

/* Writining structures into file */

# include<stdio.h>
# include<stdlib.h>

struct Address
{
    char Name[40];
    char Street[120];

    char City[20];
    long int Zip;
    char Country[20];
};

/* Prototype */

void gets1( char * ) ;

void main()
{
    struct Address add ;
    int size ;
    char file[13];
```

(Contd.)

```
    FILE *fp;

    printf("\nEnter Database file: ");
    scanf("%s",file);
    fp = fopen (file,"wb+");

    if(fp == NULL)
    {
      printf("\n File %s",file);
      perror("Error");
      exit(1);
    }
    getchar();
    printf("\n Input Name: ");
    gets1(add.Name);
    printf("\n Input Street: ");
    gets1(add.Street);
    printf("\n Input City Name: ");
    gets1(add.City);
    printf("\n Enter Country Name: ");
    gets1(add.Country);
    printf("\n Enter Pin Code: ");
    scanf("%ld", &add.Zip);
    size = sizeof(add);
    fwrite(&add,size,1,fp);
}

/* Definition of function */
void   gets1(char *s)
{
    int i ;
    char ch ;
    i = 0 ;
    ch = getchar() ;
    while(ch != '\n')
    {
      s[i] = ch ;
      i ++ ;
      ch = getchar() ;
    }
    s[i] = '\0' ;
}
```

Program 20.

```
/* prog913.c */

/* Strings and files */

# include<stdio.h>

void main()
{
    char file[13];
    FILE *fp ;
    char buffer[100];

    printf("\n Enter File Name: ");
    scanf("%s",file);
    fp = fopen ( file , "r");
    if( fp == NULL )
    {
      printf("\n File %s ",file );
      perror("Error");
      exit(1);
    }

    while(!feof(fp))
    {
      if(fgets(buffer,100,fp))
        printf("\n%s",buffer);
    }

}
```

Program 21.

```
/* prog914.c */

/* Strings and file */

# include<stdio.h>

void main()
{
```

(Contd.)

```
    char file[13];
    FILE *fp ;
    char buffer[200]=  "C is a powerful language";

    printf("\n Enter File Name: ");
    scanf("%s",file);

    fp = fopen ( file , "w");

    if( fp == NULL )
    {
      printf("\n File %s ",file );
      perror("Error");
      exit(1);
    }

    if(fputs(buffer,fp))
      printf("\nSuccessful Writing ");
}
```

Program 22.

```
/* prog915.c */

/* Strings and file */

# include<stdio.h>
# include<dirent.h>

void main()
{
    char file[13];
    char ch ;
    FILE *fp ;
    char buffer[200]=  "C language very powerful
    and useful keep with it ";

    printf("\n Enter File Name: ");
    scanf("%s",file);

    fp = fopen ( file , "r");
```

(Contd.)

```
    if( fp == NULL )
    {
      printf("\n File %s ",file );
      perror("Error");
      exit(1);
    }
    fputs(buffer,fp);
    printf("\nSuccessfully reading from file is
    completed \n ");

    rewind(fp) ; /* return the file pointer
            to start of file */
    ch = fgetc(fp);

    while(ch != EOF )
    {
      putchar(ch) ;
      ch = fgetc(fp);
    }
    fclose(fp);
}
```

Program 23.

```
/* prog916.c */

# include<stdio.h>
# include<stdlib.h>

struct Address
{
    char Name[40];
    char Street[120];

    char    City[20];
    long int Zip;
    char Country[20];
};

/* Prototype */

void gets1( char * ) ;
```

(Contd.)

```
void main()
{
    struct Address add ;
    int size ;
    int no_record ;
    int  position ;
    int n ;
    char ch ;
    char file[13];
    FILE *fp;

    printf("\nEnter Database file: ");
    gets(file);
    fp = fopen (file,"a+");

    if(fp == NULL)
    {
      printf("\n File %s",file);
      perror("Error");
      exit(1);
    }
    printf("\n Enter choice (y/n) want to add more
    record: ");
    ch = getchar();
    ch = toupper(ch) ;
    size = sizeof(add);

 while(ch == 'Y')
    {
      printf("\n Input Name: ");
      gets1(add.Name);
      printf("\n Input Street: ");
      gets1(add.Street);
      printf("\n Input City Name: ");
      gets1(add.City);
      printf("\n Enter Country Name: ");
      gets1(add.Country);
      printf("\n Enter Pin Code: ");
      scanf("%ld", &add.Zip);

      /* Writining structures into file */

      fwrite(&add,size,1,fp);
```

(Contd.)

```
      getchar();
      printf("\n Enter choice (y/n) want to add more
      record: ");
      ch = getchar();
      ch = toupper(ch) ;
    }

      /* Here we want to find number   */
      /*    of record in the file      */

    rewind(fp);
    fseek(fp,0L,2);
              /* set file pointer at end of file */
    size = ftell(fp);    /* size of file in byte */
    no_record = size / ( sizeof(add) );
    printf("\n Number of record in the file -
    >%d",no_record);

/* records are stored on the file */
/* random access  of any record  from the  file */
    printf("\n Enter Record Number want to
    seach:");
    scanf("%d", &n);
    position = (n-1)*(sizeof(add)) ;
                                /* total bytes */
    fseek(fp,position,0);

fread(&add,sizeof(add),1,fp);

/* Output section */

    puts(add.Name);
    puts(add.Street);
    puts(add.City);
    puts(add.Country);
    printf("%ld",add.Zip);
    printf("\n Press a key ");
    getchar();

}
/* Definition of function */

void   gets1(char *s)
```

(Contd.)

```
{
    int i ;
    char ch ;
    i = 0 ;
    ch = getchar() ;
    while(ch != '\n')
    {
      s[i] = ch ;
      i ++ ;
      ch = getchar() ;
    }
    s[i] = '\0' ;
}
```

Program 24.

```
/* prog917.c */

# include<stdio.h>
# include<fcntl.h>
# include<string.h>
# include<sys/stat.h>

  void main()
      {
    int fp ;          /* file pointer */

    char buffer[80] ;

fp = open("test",O_RDONLY);

      if( fp == -1 )
          {
          perror("Error");
          exit(1);
          }

         while(feof)
          {
      read(fp, buffer, 80 ) ;
      printf("\n%s",buffer);
      printf("\n Press a key");
```

(Contd.)

```
    getchar();
        }
        close(fp);
    }
```

Program 25.

```
/* prog918.c */

# include<stdio.h>
# include<fcntl.h>
# include<string.h>

void main()
{
    char buffer[] = " C is a charming language ";
    int fp ;  /* file pointer */
    fp = open("TEST",O_CREAT);
    if( fp == -1 )
    {
      perror("Error");
      exit(1);
    }
    write(fp,buffer,strlen(buffer)) ;
    close(fp);
}
```

Program 26.

```
/* prog919.c */

# include<stdio.h>
# include<fcntl.h>
# include<string.h>
# include<sys/stat.h>

void main()
{
    int fp ;             /* file pointer */

    char buffer[80] =" Enjoy with C launguage " ;
```

(Contd.)

```
    fp = creat ("test",S_IREAD  | S_IWRITE );
    if( fp == -1 )
    {
      perror("Error");
      exit(1);
    }
    write(fp, buffer, strlen(buffer) ) ;
    printf("\n Press a key");
    getchar();
    close(fp);  /* close opened file */
}
```

Program 27.

```
/* prog92.c */

# include<stdio.h>

void main()
{
    char ch ;
    FILE *fp ;    /* File pointer FILE macro  */
    fp = fopen ("test","w");
    if ( fp == NULL )
    {
      perror("ERROR");
      exit(1);
    }
    ch = getc(stdin) ;
    while(ch !='\n')/* new line character accept */
    {
      putc(ch,fp);
      ch = getc(stdin);
    }
    fclose(stdin);
    fclose(fp);
}
```

Program 28.

```
/* prog920.h */

# include<stdio.h>
# include<fcntl.h>
# include<string.h>
# include<sys/stat.h>

  void main(int argc , char *argv[])
       {
    int fp ;            /* file pointer */
    int fp1 ;           /* file pointer */
    int lenght ;
    char buffer[80] ;

    if( argc != 3)
       {
       printf("\n Missing some file ");
       exit(1);
       }

    fp = open( argv[1] , O_RDONLY);

      if( fp == -1 )
         {
         printf("\n%s",argv[1]);
         perror("Error");
         exit(1);
         }

    fp1 = open(argv[2] ,O_CREAT);
      if( fp1 == -1 )
         {
         printf("\n%s",argv[2]);
         perror("Error");
         exit(1);
         }

        read(fp, buffer, 80 ) ;
        while(!feof)
         {
```

(Contd.)

```
        lenght = strlen(buffer);
        write(fp1,buffer,lenght);
        read(fp, buffer, 80 ) ;
            }
            close(fp);    /* close file */
            close(fp1);   /* close file */
    }
```

Program 29.

```
/* prog93.c */

# include<stdio.h>

void main()
{
    char ch ;
    ch = getchar();

    /* If we replace getchar() with getche() we get
two time same character on screen this is valid in
dos environment only but the same operation is
performed using the getchar() and put  char()
functions */

    putchar(ch);
    getchar();
}
```

Program 30.

```
/* prog94.c */

# include<stdio.h>

void main()
{
    char ch ;

    /* it continously read a string when we press
return key it write the inputed string on screen */
    ch = getc(stdin);
```

(Contd.)

```
    while(ch != '\n')
                            /* new character only accept */
    {
      putc(ch,stdout);
      ch = getc(stdin);
    }
}
```

Program 31.

```
/* prog95.c */

# include<stdio.h>

void main()
{
    char ch ;
    FILE *fp ;

    fp = fopen ("DATA.DAT","r");
    if ( fp == NULL )
    {
      perror("ERROR");
      exit(1);
    }
    printf("\n");
    ch = getc(fp) ;

    while(!feof(fp) )
    {
      putc(ch, stdout);
                    /* This also may be putchar(ch) */
      ch = getc(fp);
    }
    fclose(fp);
}
```

Program 32.

```
/* prog96.c */
# include<stdio.h>
# include<string.h>
```

(Contd.)

```
void main()
{
    char infile[13], outfile[13];
    char ch ;

    FILE *input,*output ;
    printf("\n Input Source File: ");

    gets(infile);

    input = fopen(infile,"r");

    if ( input == NULL )
    {
      printf("\n File %s", infile);
      perror("Error: ");
      exit(1);
    }

    printf("\n Input Destination file: ");
    gets(outfile);
    strcat(outfile,".bak");
    output = fopen(outfile,"w");
    if ( output == NULL )
    {
      printf("\n File %s", outfile);
      perror("Error: ");
      exit(1);
    }

    ch = getc(input) ;

    while(!feof(input))
    {
      putc(ch,output);
      ch = getc(input);
    }
    fclose(input);
    fclose(output);
}
```

Program 33.

```
/* prog97.c */

/* This is equivalent to cp command of UNIX
operating system and it is also equivent to copy
command of UNIX */
# include<stdio.h>

void main(int argc, char *argv[])
{
    char ch ;
    FILE *input,*output ;

    if(argc != 3)
    {
    printf("\n Missing source or destination
    file");
      exit(1);
    }

    input = fopen(argv[1],"rb+");

    if ( input == NULL )
    {
      printf("\n File %s",argv[1]);
      perror("Error: ");
      exit(1);
    }

    output = fopen(argv[2],"wb+");

    if ( output == NULL )
    {
      printf("\n File %s",argv[2]);
      perror("Error: ");
      exit(1);
    }

    ch = getc(input) ;
    while(!feof(input) )
    {
```

(Contd.)

```
    putc(ch,output);
    ch = getc(input);
   }
   fflush(input);
   fflush(output);
   fclose(input);
   fclose(output);
}
```

Program 34.

```
/* prog98.c */

# include<stdio.h>

void main()
{
    char name[30] ;
    int age ;

    FILE  *output ;

    output = fopen("DATA","wb+");
    if ( output == NULL )
    {
      printf("\n%DATA");
      perror("Error: ");
      exit(1);
    }

    printf("\n Input name: ");
    scanf("%s",name);
    printf("\n Input age: ");
    scanf("%d",&age);
    fprintf(output,"%s",name);
    fprintf(output," %d",age);

    fflush(output);
    fclose(output);
}
```

Program 35.

```
/* prog99.c */

# include<stdio.h>
# include<string.h>
# include<stdlib.h>

void main()
{
    char file[13];
    int count = 0 ;
    char ch ;
    char name[40];
    char father_name[40];
    char roll_number[8];
    char branch[20];
    int age ;

    FILE *fp;

    printf("\nInput destination file: ");
    gets(file);

    fp = fopen(file,"w");

    if( fp == NULL )
    {
      printf("\n Destination file: %s\n",file);
      perror("Error: ");
      exit(1);
    }
    printf("\n Enter choice (y/n): ");
    ch = getchar();
    ch = toupper(ch);
    getchar();
    while(ch == 'Y')
    {
      count ++ ;
      printf("\n Input  name: ");
```

(Contd.)

```
        gets(name);
        printf("\n Input father's name: ");
        gets(father_name);
        printf("\n Input roll number: ");
        gets(roll_number);
        printf("\n Input branch: ");
        gets(branch);
        printf("\n Input age: ");
        scanf("%d",&age);

        /* Output section */

        fprintf(fp,"\n %d \n ",count);
        fputs (name, fp);
        fprintf(fp, "\n");
        fputs(father_name, fp);
        fprintf(fp, "\n");
        fputs(roll_number, fp);
        fprintf(fp, "\n");
        fputs(branch, fp);
        fprintf(fp,"\n %d \n",age);
        getchar();
        printf("\n Enter choice (y/n): ");
        ch = getchar();
        ch = toupper(ch);
        getchar();
    }
    fclose(fp);
    printf(" File successfully written");
}
```

Program 36.

```
/* remove.c */

#include <stdio.h>

void main(int argc, char *argv[])
{
    while (*++argv)
    {
      printf("\n Removing file %s", *argv);
```

(Contd.)

```
      if (remove(*argv))
        printf("Error removing %s\n", *argv);
    }
}.
```

Program 37.

```
/* rmdir.c */

# include <stdio.h>
# include <stdlib.h>
# include <errno.h>
# include<limits.h>

void main (int argc, char *argv[])
{
    char directory[_POSIX_PATH_MAX];
    if (argc == 1)  /* Display the current
directory */
    {
      getcwd(directory, _POSIX_PATH_MAX);
      puts(directory);
    }
    else if ((rmdir(argv[1])) && (errno == ENOENT))
      puts("Invalid directory");
}
```

Program 38.

```
/* search.c */
/* searches file for phrase */

#include <fcntl.h>
#include <stdio.h>
#include <string.h>
#include <stdlib.h>
#define BUFFSIZE 1024                    /* buffer
size */

char buff[BUFFSIZE];                     /* buffer */
void search(char *, int);              /* prototype */
```

(Contd.)

```
int main( int argc, char *argv[] )
{
    int inhandle, bytes;

    if(argc != 3)        /* check arguments */
    {
      printf("\n $ search filename phrase");
      exit(1);
    }
    /*  open file */
    if( (inhandle = open(argv[1], O_RDONLY )) < 0)
    {
      printf("\nCan't open file %s.", argv[1]);
      exit(1);
    }
    /* read file */
    while((bytes = read(inhandle,buff,BUFFSIZE))>0)
      search(argv[2],bytes); /* search for phrase */
    close(inhandle); /*  close file */
    printf("\nPhrase not found");
    return(0);
}

/*  search() */
/* searches buffer for phrase */
void search(char *phrase, int buflen)
{
      char *ptr, *p;
      ptr = buff;
      while( (ptr=memchr(ptr,phrase[0],buflen)) !=
      NULL)
      if( memcmp(ptr,phrase,strlen(phrase)) == 0)
                                        /* if match */
      {
        printf("First occurrance of phrase:\n");
        for(p=ptr-100; p<ptr+100; p++)
                                       /* display it */
          putchar(*p);
        exit(0);
      }
      else
        ptr++;
}
```

Program 39.

```
/* tell.c */

#include <stdio.h>
#include <fcntl.h>

void main(int argc, char *argv[])
{
    int handle;
    char buffer[512];
    int bytes_read;
    if ((handle = open(argv[1], O_RDONLY)) == -1)
      printf("Error opening %s\n", argv[1]);
    else
    {
      printf("Current file position %ld\n",
      tell(handle));

      while (bytes_read = read(handle, buffer,
      sizeof(buffer)))
        write(1, buffer, bytes_read);

      printf("Current file position %ld\n",
      tell(handle));
      close(handle);
    }
}
```

Program 40.

```
/* umask.c */

#include <stdio.h>
#include <fcntl.h>
#include <sys/stat.h>
#include <stdlib.h>
# include<sys/types.h>
# include<string.h>

void main(void)
{
```

(Contd.)

```
    int output;
    int old_setting;
    char * buffer = "Enjoy with C language: Have
    you nice day";
    old_setting = umask(S_IWRITE);

    if ((output = creat("OUTPUT.DAT", S_IWRITE))
    == -1)
    {
    fprintf(stderr, "Error creating OUTPUT.DAT\n")
      exit(1);
    }
    else
    {
if (write(output, buffer, strlen(buffer)) == -1)
fprintf(stderr, "Cannot write to file opened for
write access\n");
      else
        printf("File successfully written to\n");

      close(output);
    }

if ((output = open("OUTPUT.DAT", O_WRONLY)) == -1)
fprintf(stderr, "Error opening OUTPUT.DAT for
output\n");
    else
      printf("File successfully opened for write
      access\n");
}
```

Program 41.

```
/* utime.c */

#include <stdio.h>
#include <utime.h>

void main(int argc, char **argv)

{
int i;
```

(Contd.)

```
for (i =0; i <argc; i++)
{
    if (utime(argv[i], (struct utimbuf *) NULL))
      printf("Error setting date and time\n");
    else
      printf("Date and time stamp set of the file
      %s\n", argv[i]);
}
}
```

Program 42.

```
/* wordcnt.c */

# include<stdio.h>
# include<stdlib.h>

void main(int argc, char *argv[])
{
    FILE *fp;
    char ch;
    int white = 1; /* white space flag */
    int count = 0;   /* word count */

    if (argc != 2)
    {
      printf("\n Proper number of argument are not
      supplied ");
      exit(1);
    }

    fp = fopen (argv[1], "r");
    if( fp == NULL)
    {
      printf("\n Can not be open %s file", argv[1]);
      perror("Error: ");
      exit(1);
    }
    while ((ch = getc(fp)) != EOF)
    {
      switch(ch)
      {
```

(Contd.)

```
        case ' ':
        case '\t':
        case '\n':
          white ++;
          break;
        default:
          if (white)
          {
            white = 0;
            count++;
          }
        }
      }
      fclose (fp);
      printf("\n File %s contains %d words", argv[1],
      count);
}
```

Section VIII

Program 1.

```
/* ANIMATE.C */

/* Bouncing ball created from bit image */

#include <graphics.h>
#include <conio.h>

void main(void)
   {
   int TOP = 0, LEFT = 0;
   int RIGHT, BOTTOM;
   int RADIUS = 20;
   int driver, mode;
   int x, y, dx, dy, oldx, oldy;
   unsigned char ballbuff[2000];

   driver = DETECT;
   initgraph(&driver, &mode, "c:\\backup\\tc");

 /* Draw boundry */

  RIGHT = getmaxx();
  BOTTOM = getmaxy();

  rectangle(LEFT, TOP, RIGHT, BOTTOM);
  rectangle(LEFT+3, TOP+3, RIGHT-3, BOTTOM-3);
  rectangle(LEFT+6, TOP+6, RIGHT-6, BOTTOM-6);
```

(Contd.)

```
    x = LEFT + RADIUS + 10;
    y = TOP  + RADIUS + 10;
    setcolor(5);
    setfillstyle(HATCH_FILL, 5);
    circle(x, y, RADIUS);
    floodfill(x, y, 5);

  /* place image in memory */

    getimage(x-RADIUS, y-RADIUS, x+RADIUS, y+RADIUS,
     ballbuff);
     dx = 2;
     dy = 2;
     while ( !kbhit() )
        {

  /* Put memory image on screen */

       putimage(x-RADIUS, y-RADIUS, ballbuff,
        COPY_PUT);
       oldx = x; oldy = y;
       x += dx;  y += dy;
       if( x<=LEFT+RADIUS+2 || x>=RIGHT-RADIUS-2 )
        dx = -dx;
       if( y<=TOP+RADIUS+2 || y>=BOTTOM-RADIUS-2 )
        dy = -dy;
       putimage(oldx-RADIUS, oldy-RADIUS, ballbuff,
        XOR_PUT);
        }
     closegraph();
     }
```

Program 2.

```
/* aspect.c */
/* shows use of getaspectratio() */

#include <graphics.h>
# include <conio.h>

#define LEFT    100
#define TOP       0
```

(Contd.)

```
#define RIGHT   300
#define BOT     200
#define HEIGHT  (BOT-TOP)
#define WIDTH   (RIGHT-LEFT)
#define XC      (LEFT+WIDTH/2)
#define YC      (TOP+HEIGHT/2)

void main(void)
   {
     int driver, mode;
     int xradius;
     int yradius;
     int xAspect, yAspect;
     float ratio1;
     float ratio2;

     driver = EGA;
     mode = EGAHI;
     initgraph( &driver, &mode, "c:\\tc\\bgi" );
     rectangle(LEFT, TOP, RIGHT, BOT);
     xradius = WIDTH/2;
     yradius = HEIGHT/2;
     ellipse(XC, YC, 0, 360, xradius, yradius);
     getaspectratio(&xAspect, &yAspect);
                                      /* get aspect ratio */
     printf("\n %d",xAspect);
     printf("\n %d",yAspect);

     ratio1 = (float)xAspect / (float)yAspect;
                                         /* calculate it */
     printf("\n %f", ratio1);
     ratio2 = (float)yAspect / (float)xAspect;
                                         /* calculate it */
     printf("\n %f", ratio2);
     xradius = xradius*ratio2;
     ellipse(XC, YC, 0, 360, xradius, yradius);

     getch();
     closegraph();
```

Program 3.

```
/* BARTXT.C */
/************************************************/
/*     This program draws bar charts            */
/*     without using graphics.                  */
/*     To blink a text cprintf                  */
/*     function requires.                       */
/************************************************/

# include<conio.h>
# include<stdio.h>

  void main()
    {
     int i,j;
     clrscr();
     textmode(80) ;     /* Set 80 column screen */
     for(i = 5; i <= 15 ;i++)
    {
   gotoxy(1,i);
   putchar(219);
   gotoxy(2,i);
   putchar(219);

   gotoxy(5,i);
   putchar(219);
   gotoxy(6,i);
   putchar(219);

   gotoxy(10,i);
   putchar(219);
   gotoxy(11,i);
   putchar(219);

   gotoxy(15,i);
   putchar(219);
   gotoxy(16,i);
   putchar(219);

   gotoxy(20,i);
   putchar(219);
```

(Contd.)

```
gotoxy(21,i);
putchar(219);

gotoxy(25,i);
putchar(219);
gotoxy(26,i);
putchar(219);

gotoxy(30,i);
putchar(219);
gotoxy(31,i);
putchar(219);

gotoxy(35,i);
putchar(219);
gotoxy(36,i);
putchar(219);

gotoxy(40,i);
putchar(219);
gotoxy(41,i);
putchar(219);

gotoxy(45,i);
putchar(219);
gotoxy(46,i);
putchar(219);

gotoxy(50,i);
putchar(219);
gotoxy(51,i);
putchar(219);
  }
 gotoxy(1,16);

 for(i = 0 ; i<50 ;i++)
  {
   putchar(223);
  }
 textbackground(WHITE);
 textcolor(RED | BLINK );
 gotoxy(20,12);
```

(Contd.)

```
    cprintf("\n * BAR - CHART * ");
    gotoxy(20,20);
    textcolor(YELLOW | BLINK );
    cprintf("\n Press a Key ");
  //  getch();
   }
```

Program 4.

```
/* brescir.c */

/* Drawing circle using bresenham's algorithm */

# include<graphics.h>
# include<conio.h>
# include<stdio.h>

 void plot_circle(int xc, int yc, int x, int y);
 void Bresen_circle(int xc, int yc, int r);

 void Bresen_circle(int xc, int yc, int r)
    {
    int x, y;
    int p;
    int driver = DETECT;
    int gmode;
    initgraph(&driver, &gmode, "c:\\tc\\bgi");

    x = 0;
    y = r;
    p = 3 - 2 * r;

    while(x < y)
     {
       plot_circle(xc, yc, x, y);
        if(p < 0)
          p = p + 4 * x + 6;
          else
      {
       p = p + 4 * ( x - y ) + 10;
       y -= 1;
     }
     x += 1;
```

(Contd.)

```
    }
   if(x == y)
    plot_circle(xc, yc, x, y);
  }

void plot_circle(int xc, int yc, int x, int y)
  {
   putpixel(xc+x, yc+y, RED);
   putpixel(xc-x, yc+y, RED);
   putpixel(xc+x, yc-y, RED);
   putpixel(xc-x, yc-y, RED);

   putpixel(xc+y, yc+x, RED);
   putpixel(xc-y, yc+x, RED);
   putpixel(xc+y, yc-x, RED);
   putpixel(xc-y, yc+x, RED);
  }

  void main()
    {
  int xc = 300, yc = 200;
  int r = 50;
  Bresen_circle(xc, yc, r);
  getch();
    }
```

Program 5.

```
/* bresen.c */

/* Drawing line using bresenham's algorithm */

# include<graphics.h>
# include<conio.h>
# include<stdio.h>

 void Bresen(int x1, int y1, int x2, int y2)
   {
  int dx, dy;
  int c1, c2, x, y;
  int p;
  int xend, yend;
```

(Contd.)

```
int driver = DETECT;
int gmode;
initgraph(&driver, &gmode, "c:\\tc\\bgi");

dx = abs(x2 - x1);
dy = abs(y2 - y1);
p = 2 * dy - dx;
c1 = 2 * dy;
c2 = 2 * (dy - dx);

if (x1 > x2)
{
  x = x2;
  y = y2;
  xend = x1;
}
else
{
 x = x1;
 y = y1;
 xend = x2;
}
putpixel(x,y, RED);

while(x < xend)
 {
  x = x+1;
  if ( p < 0 )
  p = p + c1;
  else
  {
    y = y +1;
    p = p+ c2;
  }
   putpixel(x,y, RED);
  }
}

void main()
 {
   int x1 = 300, y1 = -100;
   int x2 = 150, y2 = 10;
```

(Contd.)

```
    printf("\n Input first coordinate: ");
    scanf("\n %d%d", &x1, &y1);

    printf("\n Input second coordinate: ");
    scanf("\n %d%d", &x1, &y1);

    Bresen(x1, y1, x2, y2);
  getch();
    }
```

Program 6.

```
/* dda.c */

/* Drawing line using digital differential
algorithm */

# include<graphics.h>
# include<conio.h>
# include<stdio.h>
# define Limit 0.5

 void DDA(int x1, int y1, int x2, int y2)
   {
   int x3, y3;
   int dx, dy, step;
   float xi, yi, x, y;
   float d1, d2;
   int k;
   int driver = DETECT;
   int gmode;
   initgraph(&driver, &gmode, "c:\\tc\\bgi");

   dx = x2 - x1;
   dy = y2 - y1;

   if(abs(dx) > abs(dy))
    step = abs(dx);
    else
     step = abs(dy);

     xi = (float) dx/ (float) step;
```

(Contd.)

```
yi = (float) dy/ (float) step;

x = x1;
y = y1;

x3 = x;
y3 = y;

putpixel(x3, y3, RED);

 for (k = 1; k <step; k++)
  {
  d1 = x - x3;
  d2 = y - y3;

  if (d1 >= Limit)
   x3 = x3 + 1;
   else
     {
 x = xi + x;
 x3 = x;
     }
   if (d2 >= Limit)
    y3 = y3 + 1;
    else
    {
y = yi + y;
y3 = y;
    }
    putpixel (x3, y3, RED);
    }
}

void main()
  {
   int x1, y1;
   int x2, y2;

  printf("\n Input starting point: ");
  scanf("%d%d", &x1, &y1);
  printf("\n Input ending point: ");
  scanf("%d%d", &x2, &y2);
```

(Contd.)

```
  DDA(x1, y1, x2, y2);
  getch();
  closegraph();
  }
```

Program 7.

```
/* FONT.C */
/*************************************************/
/* Gives  demo of deffirent FONTS support by   */
/* Turbo-C/C++ Compiler in graphics mode also */
/* size of text as well as direction in xy     */
/* coordinates plane                           */
/*************************************************/

# include<graphics.h>
# include<dos.h>
# include<stdlib.h>
# include<conio.h>

    /* Default font 8x8 bit mapped */
    /* Other are stroked fonts     */

  char *font_name[] = {

      "DEFAULT_FONT  " ,
      "TRIPLEX_FONT  " ,
      "SMALL_FONT          ",
      "SANS_SERIF_FONT           ",
      "GOTHIC_FONT          "
      "SCRIPT_FONT     ",
      "SIMPLEX_FONT  ",
      "TRIPLEXSCR_FONT ",
      "COMPLEX_FONT  ",
      "EUROPEAN_FONT    ",
      "BOLD_FONT  "
      } ;

void main()
      {
      int gd = DETECT ;
      int gm ;
```

(Contd.)

```
        int num ,i;
        int x ,y ;

       initgraph(&gd, &gm,"C:\\backup\\tc");

        for(i = DEFAULT_FONT ; i <BOLD_FONT; i++)
        {

        settextstyle(i,0,0);
        outtextxy(50,50,font_name[i]);
//      delay(1000);
        getch();
           clearviewport();

        }
        y = getmaxy();
        x = getmaxx();

          settextstyle(0,1,1);
              /* 1 as second parameter for vertical */
          outtextxy(x-100,10," Press a Key to back in
          text mode");
          getch();
          closegraph() ;

          printf("\n Press a key to display
          coordinates ");
          getch();
          printf("\n Size of X axis in graphics mode =
          %d",x);
          printf("\n Size of Y axis in graphics mode =
          %d",y);
          printf("\n Press a Key ");

         getch();
         closegraph();
        }
```

Program 8.

```
/* fractal.c */

# include<stdio.h>
# include<graphics.h>
```

(Contd.)

```
# include<stdlib.h>
# include<time.h>
# include<math.h>
# include<conio.h>

# define X0 320
# define Y0 240
# define PI 3.14159
# define NUME 30
# define DENOM 100
# define NUMBER 7
# define RAD 3.0
# define DELTHETA 0.1
# define SEGS 60
# define REDUX 3
# define MIN 1

display1(int size, float theta, int x, int y);

void display (int size, int x0, int y0)
   {
    int i;
    if (kbhit())
     exit(0);
     for(i = 0; i < NUMBER; i++)
      {
      float theta = i*2*PI/NUMBER;
      int x = x0;
      int y = y0;
      moveto (x,y);
      display1(size, theta, x, y);
     }
   }
  display1(int size, float theta, int x, int y)
     {
       int chng;
       int j;
       int newsize;
       for(j = 0; j < size; j++)
   {
        chng = (random(DENOM) < NUME) ? -1 : 1;
      theta = theta + chng * DELTHETA;
      x = x + RAD* sin(theta);
```

(Contd.)

```
y = y + RAD* cos(theta);
if(size<4)
setcolor(RED);
else
if(size< 13)
setcolor(GREEN);
else
if(size< 40)
setcolor(LIGHTGREEN);
else
setcolor(YELLOW);
lineto(x,y);
}
if (size> MIN)
{
newsize = size/REDUX;
display(newsize, x,y);
}
}

void main()
{
int x, y;
int size;
int driver, gmode;
driver = VGA;
gmode = VGAHI;
initgraph(&driver, &gmode, "c:\\tc");
randomize();
x = X0;
y = Y0;
size = SEGS;
display(size, x, y);
getch();
closegraph();
}
```

Program 9.

```
/* getpoint.c */

# include<stdio.h>
# include<conio.h>
```

(Contd.)

```
# include<io.h>
# include<dos.h>

char getpoint( int x, int y)
  {
     union REGS reg;

     reg.h.ah = 13;
     reg.x.dx = y;
     reg.x.cx = x;
     reg.h.bh = 0;
     int86(16, &reg, &reg);
     return (reg.h.al);
  }

 void main()
 {
     int x, y;
     printf("\n Input the values of x and y: ");
     scanf("%d%d", &x, &y);
     printf("\n Information: %c", getpoint(x,y));
  }
```

Program 10.

```
/* getputt.c */
/*********************************************/
/* Gives  the demo of some text mode function   */
/* which will work like graphics function in 'C'*/
/* display character V at the screen and which made*/
/* from character v and WELCOME word display in it */
/* when we press a key  a portion cut and paste */
/* operation performed and message cut-paste is */
/* display  with blinking                       */
/*********************************************/

# include<stdio.h>
# include<conio.h>
# include<io.h>

 void main()
     {
```

(Contd.)

```
        register int i;
        register int j;
        char buffer[1000];
        textmode(80);  /* text mode 80 column */
        clrscr();

/* Produce character V on the screen */

        for( i = 1, j = 1 ; j < 24; i++ , j++)
     {
      gotoxy(i,j);
      cprintf("v");
      }

      for(i = i , j = j ;  j > 0; i++, j--)
       {
        gotoxy(i,j);
        cprintf("v");
       }

  /* Back ground color setting */

      textbackground(LIGHTBLUE);
      textcolor(RED);              /* Set text color */
      gotoxy(20,12);
      textcolor(GREEN | BLINK );
                 /* Set text color with blink */

      textbackground( BLACK);
                     /* Set back ground color */
      cprintf("WELCOME ") ;
      gotoxy(60,23);
      printf("\n Press a key");
      getch();
      gettext(20,20,28,24,buffer);  /* Get text */
      gotoxy(60,23);
      printf("\n Press a key");
      getch();
      clrscr();
      gotoxy(60,23);
      printf("\n Press a key");
      getch();
```

(Contd.)

```
puttext(20,15,28,19,buffer);  /* Put text */
gotoxy(20,6);
cprintf("cut paste");
gotoxy(60,23);
printf("\n Press a key");
getch();
textmode(LASTMODE); /* Last mode of the screen
*/
}
```

Program 11.

```
/* GRAPHTXT.C */

/* Plot function y = x ^ 2 /5 +1
   without graphics function     */

# include<conio.h>
# include<stdio.h>
# include<math.h>

   void main()
     {
     float  x;
     float y;
     int i, j;

     clrscr();

     for( x = 0.5; x < 10 ; x+=0.5)
        {
    y = pow(x,2)/5 +1 + 0.5;
    gotoxy(x,y);
    putchar(248);
        }

    gotoxy(1,1);
    for( i= 0; i<40 ; i++)
       {
        putchar(223);
       }
       printf("  X-axis");
```

(Contd.)

```
        for( j = 1 ; j < 22 ; j++)
          {
           gotoxy(1,j);
           putchar(219);
          }

         printf("\n\n Y-axis");
         gotoxy(13,10);
         printf("<=============== y = x^2/5 +1 ");
         gotoxy(40,23);
         printf("\n Press a Key ");
         getch();
         }
```

Program 12.

```
/* GRDEMO.C */

/* Gives demo of the most of the graphics   */
/* functions supported by Turbo-C/C++       */

# include<string.h>
# include<stdlib.h>
# include<io.h>
# include<process.h>
# include<stdio.h>
# include<graphics.h>
# include<conio.h>
# include<malloc.h>

/* Prototypes */

int huge detectEGA() ;
void checkerrors();

/* Global parameter */

int poly2[16] ;

int i ;
int gd,gm;
struct arccoordstype arcinfo;
```

(Contd.)

```
int stangle = 45 ;
int endangle = 270;
int radius = 100 ;
int midx ;
int midy ;
char sstr [80];
char estr[80];
int xasp ;
int yasp ;
char pattern[8] = {
    0x00,0x70,0x20,0x27,0x24,0x24,0x07,0x00 };
char *driver ;
int bkcolor ;
char bkname[40];
int color ;
char color_name[40];

struct fillsettingstype fill_info ;
char patstr[40];
char colstr[40];

/* Name of the fill pattern supported */

char *f_name[] ={
        "EMPTY_FILL",
        "SOLID_FILL ",
        "LINE_FILL ",
        "LTSLASH_FILL ",
        "SLASH_FILL",
        "BKSLASH_FILL ",
        "LTBKSLASH_FILL",
        "HATCH_FILL",
        "XHATCH_FILL",
        "INTERLEAVE_FILL",
        "WIDE_DOT_FILL ",
        "CLOSE_DOT_FILL ",
        "USER_FILL "
          };

char num_name[80];
char mode_name[80];
int mode ;
```

(Contd.)

```
struct linesettingstype line_info ;
char lpattern[80];
char lwidth[80];
char lstyle[80];
char *l_name [] = {
            "SOLID_LINE   ",
            "DOTTED_LINE  ",
            "CENTER_LINE  ",
            "DASHED_LINE  ",
            "USERBIT_LINE "
           };

char modestr[80];

int low ;
int high ;
char mrange[80];

struct palettetype pal ;
char psize[80] ;
char pval[80];

struct textsettingstype text_info ;
char fontstr[80];
char sizestr[80];
char dirstr[80];
char hjuststr[80];
char vjuststr[80];
int ht ;

char *font[] = {
         "DEFAULT_FONT  " ,
         "TRIPLEX_FONT  " ,
         "SMALL_FONT             ",
         "SANS_SERIF_FONT         ",
         "GOTHIC_FONT            "
         "SCRIPT_FONT    ",
         "SIMPLEX_FONT   ",
         "TRIPLEXSCR_FONT ",
         "COMPLEX_FONT   ",
         "EUROPEAN_FONT  ",
         "BOLD_FONT   "
       };
```

(Contd.)

```
char *dir[] = {
            "HORIZ_DIR",
            "VERT_DIR"
            };
char *hjust[] = {
         "LEFT_TEXT     ",
         "CENTER_TEXT   ",
         "RIGHT_TEXT    ",
             };

char *vjust[] = {
         "BOTTOM_TEXT  ",
         "TOP_TEXT "
             };

struct viewporttype view_info ;

char *clip[] = {
         "ON",
         "OFF"
            };

char topstr[80];
char botstr[80];
char clipstr[80];
int error_code ;
char msg[80];
unsigned int size ;
char *buffer;

int userfont ;
char *color_name1[] = {
            " BLACK",
            " BLUE  ",
            " GREEN ",
            " CYAN  ",
            " RED   ",
            " MAGENTA",
            " BROWN " ,
            " LIGHTGRAY",
            " DARKGRAY ",
            " LIGHTBLUE",
```

(Contd.)

```
              " LIGHTGREEN",
              " LIGHTCYAN ",
              " LIGHTRED  ",
              " LIGHTMAGENTA",
              " YELLOW",
              " WHITE "
             };

char *cga_color_name1[] = {
              "CGA_LIGHTGREEN",
              "CGA_LIGHTRED " ,
              "CGA_YELLOW  " ,
              "CGA_LIGHTCYAN ",
              "CGA_LIGHTMAGENTA",
              "CGA_WHITE " ,
              "CGA_GREEN" ,
              "CGA_RED  " ,
              "CGA_BROWN ",
              "CGA_CYAN  ",
              "CGA_MAGENTA ",
              "CGA_LIGHTGRAY"
          };

char *ega_color_name1[] = {
              " EGA_BLACK    " ,
              " EGA_BLUE      " ,
              " EGA_GREEN     " ,
              " EGA_CYAN      ",
              " EGA_RED       " ,
              " EGA_MAGENTA   " ,
              " EGA_BROWN     " ,
              " EGA_LIGHTGRAY "
             };
char *light_color_name2[] = {
              " EGA_DARKGRAY  " ,
              " EGA_LIGHTBLUE " ,
              " EGA_LIGHTGREEN" ,
              " EGA_LIGHTCYAN " ,
              " EGA_LIGHTRED  " ,
              " EGA_LIGHTMAGENTA",
              " EGA_YELLOW       ",
```

(Contd.)

```
          " EGA_WHITE         "
          };

char *line_name[] = {
         "SOLID_LINE",
         "DOTTED_LINE",
         "CENTER_LINE" ,
         "DASHED_LINE" ,
         "USERBIT_LINE"
            };

/* Declaration ends here */

void main()
{
    int choice ;

    choice = choice_fun();
    do
    {

      switch(choice)
      {
      case 1 :
        init();
        bar_fun() ;
        press_key();
        break ;

      case 2 :
        init();
        bar3d_fun() ;
        press_key();
        break ;

      case 3 :
        init();
        ellipse_fun() ;
        press_key();
        break ;
```

(Contd.)

```
case 4 :
  init();
  fil_ellipse_fun();
  press_key();
  break ;

case 5 :
  init();
  poly_fun() ;
  press_key();
  break ;

case 6 :
  init();
  fil_poly_fun();
  press_key();
  break ;

case 7 :
  init();
  flood_fun() ;
  press_key();
  break ;

case 8 :
  init();
  arc_fun() ;
  press_key();
  break ;

case 9 :
  init();
  arc_coord() ;
  press_key();
  break ;

case 10:
  init();
  aspect_ratio_fun();
  press_key();
  break ;
```

(Contd.)

```
case 11:
  init();
  pat_fun();
  press_key();
  break ;

case 12:
  init();
  driver_fun();
  press_key();
  break ;

case 13:
  init();
  back_color();
  press_key();
  break ;

case 14:
  init();
  draw_color();
  press_key();
  break ;

case 15 :
  init();
  pat_find_fun() ;
  press_key();
  break ;

case 16 :
  init();
  mode_string() ;
  press_key();
  break ;

case 17:
  init();
  line_info_fun();
  press_key();
  break ;
```

(Contd.)

```
case 18:
  init();
  max_mode_fun();
  press_key();
  break ;

case 19:
  init();
  get_mode_fun();
  press_key();
  break ;

case 20:
  init();
  get_pal_fun();
  press_key();
  break ;

case 21:
  init();
  pal_size_fun();
  press_key();
  break ;

case 22:
  init();
  text_set_fun();
  press_key();
  break ;

case 23:
  init();
  view_cor_fun();
  press_key();
  break ;

case 24:
  init();
  cur_pos_fun() ;
  press_key();
  break ;
```

(Contd.)

```
case 25:
  init();
  set_l_style_fun();
  press_key();
  break ;

case 26:
  init();
  image_size_fun();
  press_key();
  break ;

case 27:
  init();
  user_font_fun();
  press_key();
  break ;

case 28:
  init();
  line_rel_fun();
  press_key();
  break ;

case 29:
  init();
  mov_fun() ;
  press_key();
  break ;

case 30:
  init();
  output_fun();
  press_key();
  break ;

case 31:
  init();
  pie_fun();
  press_key();
  break ;
```

(Contd.)

```
case 32 :
  init();
  rest_fun();
  press_key();
  break ;

case 33:
  init();
  sector_fun();
  press_key();
  break ;

case 34 :
  init();
  fill_pattern_fun();
  press_key();
  break ;

case 35 :
  init();
  driver_set_fun();
  press_key();
  break ;

case 36 :
  init();
  col_fun();
  press_key();
  break ;

case 37 :
  init();
  ega_col_fun();
  press_key();
  break ;

case 38 :
  init();
  light_col_fun();
  press_key();
```

(Contd.)

```
        case 39 :
          init();
          cga_col_fun();
          press_key();
          break ;

        case 40 :
          init();
          line_style_fun();
          press_key();
          break ;

        default :
          break ;
        }
        choice = choice_fun();
    } while( choice != 0 );
}

/* Function declaration section */

/* Bar chart */

bar_fun()
{
    cleardevice();
    setcolor(RED);
    bar( midx,midy,midx/2,midy/4);
    settextstyle(1,0,4);
    outtextxy(midx,5,"Bar Chart");
    return ;
}

/*Bar chart 3-D */

bar3d_fun()
{
    cleardevice();
    setcolor(RED);
    bar3d(50,50,200,250,50,1);
    settextstyle(1,0,4);
    outtextxy(midx,5,"Bar 3-D Chart");
```

(Contd.)

```
    return ;
}

/* Ellipse function */

ellipse_fun()
{
    cleardevice();
    ellipse(midx,midy, 0, 360, 75,50);
    settextstyle(1,0,4);
    outtextxy(midx,5,"ELLIPSE");
    return ;
}

/* Fill ellipse function */

fil_ellipse_fun()
{
    cleardevice();
    fillellipse( midx,midy, 75,50);
    settextstyle(1,0,4);
    outtextxy(midx,5,"FILL ELLIPSE");
    return ;
}

/* Poly function */

poly_fun()
{
    midx = getmaxx()/2;
    midy = getmaxy()/2 ;

    poly2[0] = midx-43;
    poly2[1] = midy-25;

    poly2[2] = midx+43;
    poly2[3] = midy-25;

    poly2[4] = midx;
    poly2[5] = midy+50;
```

(Contd.)

```
    poly2[6] = midx-43;
    poly2[7] = midy-25;

    poly2[8] = midx-43;
    poly2[9] = midy+25;
    poly2[10] = midx+43;
    poly2[11] = midy+25;

    poly2[12] = midx;
    poly2[13] = midy-50 ;

    poly2[14] = midx-43;
    poly2[15] = midy+25;
    setcolor(RED);
    circle(midx,midy,30);
    setcolor(GREEN);
    drawpoly(8,poly2);
    circle(midx,midy,25);
    setcolor(YELLOW);
    circle(midx,midy,20);
    setcolor(RED);
    circle(midx,midy,15);
    setcolor(GREEN);
    circle(midx,midy,10);
    settextstyle(1,0,4);
    outtextxy(midx-60,midy+75,"WELCOME");
    settextstyle(1,0,4);
    outtextxy(midx,5,"POLY FUN");
    return ;
}

/* Fill poly function */

fil_poly_fun()
{
    cleardevice();
    poly_fun();
    press_key();
    init();
    drawpoly(8, poly2);
    fillpoly(8, poly2);
    settextstyle(1,0,4);
```

(Contd.)

```
    outtextxy(midx,5,"POLY FILL");
    return ;
}
/* Flood fill function */

flood_fun()
{
    cleardevice();
    circle(midx,midy,midy/3);
    settextstyle(1,0,4);
    outtextxy(midx,5,"CIRCLE");
    press_key();
    init();
    circle(midx,midy,midy/3);
    floodfill(midx,midy,RED);
    settextstyle(1,0,4);
    outtextxy(midx,5,"FLOOD FILL");
    return ;
}

/* Arc function */

arc_fun()
{
    arc(midx,midy,stangle,endangle,50);
    settextstyle(1,0,4);
    outtextxy(midx-50,midy+75,"A R C");
    return ;
}

/* Show arc coordinate */

arc_coord()
{
    arc(midx,midy,stangle,endangle,50);
    getarccoords(&arcinfo);
    sprintf(sstr, "*-(%d,
%d)",arcinfo.xstart,arcinfo.ystart);
    sprintf(estr, "*-(%d,
%d)",arcinfo.xend,arcinfo.yend);
    outtextxy(arcinfo.xstart,arcinfo.ystart,sstr);
    outtextxy(arcinfo.xend,arcinfo.yend,estr);
    settextstyle(1,0,4);
```

(Contd.)

```
    outtextxy(midx,5,"ARC Coordinate");
    return ;
 }

/* Show aspect ratio */

aspect_ratio_fun()
{
    cleardevice();
    circle(midx,midy,100);
    setcolor(getmaxcolor());
    getaspectratio(&xasp,&yasp);
    circle(midx,midy,100);
    settextstyle(1,0,4);
    outtextxy(midx-75,5,"Aspect ratio of CIRCLE ");
    press_key();
    init();
    cleardevice();
    setaspectratio(xasp/2,yasp);
    circle(midx,midy,100);
    settextstyle(1,0,4);
    outtextxy(midx-75,5,"Aspect ratio of X-Axis/2
");
    press_key();
    init();
    cleardevice();
    setaspectratio(xasp,yasp/2);
    circle(midx,midy,100);
    settextstyle(1,0,4);
    outtextxy(midx-75,5,"Aspect ratio of Y-Axis/2
");
    return ;
}

/* Pattern function */

pat_fun()
{
    cleardevice();
    bar(0,0,midx,midy);
    settextstyle(1,0,4);
    outtextxy(midx-75,5,"FILL PATTERN OF ");
    press_key();
```

(Contd.)

```
    init();
    setfillpattern(pattern,RED);
    cleardevice();
    bar(midx/2,0,midx,midy);
    getfillpattern(pattern);
    pattern[4] -= 1;
    pattern[5] -= 3;
    pattern[6] += 3;
    pattern[7] -= 4 ;

    setfillpattern(pattern,getmaxcolor());
    bar(0,0,midx,midy);
    settextstyle(1,0,4);
    outtextxy(midx-75,5,"FILL PATTERN");
    return ;
}

/* Driver name  function */

driver_fun()
{
    cleardevice();
    settextstyle(1,0,4);
    outtextxy(midx-75,5,"DEVICE DRIVER");
    driver = getdrivername();
    outtextxy(midx,midy,driver);
    return ;
}

/* Color background */

back_color()
{
    /* Centering text on the display */
    cleardevice();
    settextjustify(CENTER_TEXT,CENTER_TEXT);
    bkcolor = getbkcolor() ;
    itoa(bkcolor,bkname,10);
    strcat(bkname," is the current back ground
    color");
    outtextxy(midx,midy,bkname);
    settextstyle(1,0,4);
    outtextxy(midx-75,10,"BKCOLOR");
```

(Contd.)

```
    return ;
 }

 /*  Drawing color find */
 draw_color()
 {
    /* Centering text on the display */

    cleardevice();
    settextjustify(CENTER_TEXT,CENTER_TEXT);
    color = getcolor() ;
    itoa(color,color_name,10);
    strcat(color_name," is the current drawing
    color");
    outtextxy(midx,midy,color_name);
    settextstyle(1,0,4);
    outtextxy(midx-75,10,"DRAWING-COLOR");
    return ;
 }

 /* Find filling pattern */

 pat_find_fun()
 {
    /* centering text on the display */
    cleardevice();
    settextjustify(CENTER_TEXT,CENTER_TEXT);
    getfillsettings( &fill_info );

    sprintf(patstr, "%s is the fill style
    ",f_name[fill_info.pattern]);
    sprintf(colstr, "%d is the fill info color
    ",f_name[fill_info.color] );

    settextjustify(CENTER_TEXT,CENTER_TEXT);
    outtextxy(midx,midy,patstr);
    outtextxy(midx, midy+ 2* textheight("W"),colstr
 );
    settextstyle(1,0,4);
    outtextxy(midx-75,10,"FILLED PATTERN");
    return ;
 }
```

(Contd.)

```
/* Get mode and strings */

mode_string()
{
    cleardevice();
    mode = getgraphmode();
    sprintf(num_name, "%d is the current mode
    number ",mode);
    sprintf(mode_name, "%s is the current graphics
    mode",getmodename(mode));

    /* Display the information */

    settextjustify(CENTER_TEXT,CENTER_TEXT);
    outtextxy(midx,midy,num_name);
    outtextxy(midx, midy+ 2*
    textheight("W"),mode_name );
    settextstyle(1,0,4);
    outtextxy(midx-75,10,"MODE");
    return ;
}

/* Line information */

line_info_fun()
{
    cleardevice();
    getlinesettings( &line_info );

    /* convert information into strings */

    sprintf(lstyle, "%s is the line style
    ",l_name[line_info.linestyle]);
    sprintf(lpattern, "0x%X is the current line
    pattern", l_name[line_info.upattern]);

    sprintf(lwidth, "%d is the line thickness
    ",l_name[line_info.thickness]);

    /* Display the information */

    settextjustify(CENTER_TEXT,CENTER_TEXT);
    outtextxy(midx,midy,lstyle);
```

(Contd.)

```
    outtextxy(midx, midy+ 2*
    textheight("W"),lpattern );
    outtextxy(midx, midy+ 4*
    textheight("W"),lwidth);
    settextstyle(1,0,4);
    outtextxy(midx-75,10,"LINE SETTINGS USED");
    return ;
}.

/* Tells about maximum mode */

max_mode_fun()
{
    cleardevice();
    sprintf(modestr,"0...%d this driver support
    ",getmaxmode());

    /* Display the information */

    settextjustify(CENTER_TEXT,CENTER_TEXT);
    outtextxy(midx,midy,modestr);
    settextstyle(1,0,4);
    outtextxy(midx-75,10,"MAXIMUM MODE ");
    return ;
}

/* Getmoderange */

get_mode_fun()
{
    cleardevice();
    gd = DETECT ;
    getmoderange(gd,&low,&high)

/* convert mode range information into strings */

    sprintf(mrange,"this driver support modes ->%d
    %d",low, high);

    /* display the information */

    settextjustify(CENTER_TEXT,CENTER_TEXT);
    outtextxy(midx,midy,mrange);
```

(Contd.)

```
    settextstyle(1,0,4);
    outtextxy(midx-75,10,"DRIVER SUPPORT  MODES "),
    return ;
}
/*  Get palette */

get_pal_fun()
{
    cleardevice();
    getpalette( &pal);
    sprintf(psize,"this palette has %d,modifiable
    entries",pal.size);
    settextjustify(CENTER_TEXT,CENTER_TEXT);
    outtextxy(midx,midy,psize);
    settextstyle(1,0,4);
    outtextxy(midx-75,10,"PALETTE");
    return ;
}

/* Get palette size */

pal_size_fun()
{
    cleardevice();
    sprintf(psize,"this palette has %d,modifiable
    entries",getpalettesize());
    settextjustify(CENTER_TEXT,CENTER_TEXT);
    outtextxy(midx,midy,psize);
    settextstyle(1,0,4);
    outtextxy(midx-75,10,"PALETTE-SIZE");
    return ;
}

/* Get information about current text settings */

text_set_fun()
{
    cleardevice();
    gettextsettings( &text_info);
    sprintf(fontstr,"%s is the text style ",
    font[text_info.font]);
    sprintf(dirstr,"%s is the direction " ,
    dir[text_info.direction]);
```

(Contd.)

```
    sprintf(sizestr,",%d is the size of text
    ",text_info.charsize);
    sprintf(hjuststr,"%s is the horizontal
    justification",hjust[text_info.horiz]);
    sprintf(vjuststr,"%s is the vertical
    justification",vjust[text_info.vert]);

    /* Display the information */

    ht = textheight("W");
    settextjustify(CENTER_TEXT,CENTER_TEXT);
    outtextxy(midx,midy,fontstr);
    outtextxy(midx, midy+ 2* ht,dirstr );
    outtextxy(midx, midy+ 4* ht,sizestr);
    outtextxy(midx, midy+ 6* ht,hjuststr );
    outtextxy(midx, midy+ 8* ht,vjuststr);
    settextstyle(1,0,4);
    outtextxy(midx-75,10,"TEXT SETTINGS ");
    return ;
}

/* Gives coordinates of viewport setting */

view_cor_fun()
{
    cleardevice();
    getviewsettings( &view_info);
    sprintf(topstr,"(%d, %d) left upper top
    viewport corner", view_info.left,
    view_info.top);
    sprintf(botstr,"(%d , %d)lower right bottom "
    view_info.right,view_info.bottom);
    sprintf(clipstr,",Clipping is turned %s
    ",clip[view_info.clip]);

    /* Display the information */

    ht = textheight("W");
    settextjustify(CENTER_TEXT,CENTER_TEXT);
    outtextxy(midx,midy,topstr);
    outtextxy(midx, midy+ 2* ht,botstr);
    outtextxy(midx, midy+ 4* ht,clipstr);
    settextstyle(1,0,4);
```

(Contd.)

```
    outtextxy(midx-75,10,"VIEW PORT COORDINATE");
    return ;
}

/* Find current cursor postion  getx, gety */

cur_pos_fun()
{
    cleardevice();
    moveto(getmaxx()/2,getmaxy()/2); /* set the
    center of screen */
    sprintf(msg,"<--( %d, %d ) is the here
    ",getx(), gety());

    /* Display the information */

    ht = textheight("W");
    settextjustify(CENTER_TEXT,CENTER_TEXT);
    outtextxy(midx,midy,msg);
    settextstyle(1,0,4);
    outtextxy(midx-75,10,"CURRENT CURSOR
    POSITION");
    return ;
}

/* Set line style */

set_l_style_fun()
{
    cleardevice();
    setlinestyle(DOTTED_LINE , 0 , 3);
    line ( 0,0,2* midx,2*midy);
    settextjustify(CENTER_TEXT,CENTER_TEXT);
    outtextxy(midx/2,midy/3,"Before default values
    stored ");
    settextstyle(1,0,4);
    outtextxy(midx-75,10,"LINE STYLE SETTINGS");
    press_key();
    init();
    cleardevice();
    graphdefaults();
    line(0,0,2*midx,2*midy);  /* line after default
    settings */
```

(Contd.)

```
    settextjustify(CENTER_TEXT,CENTER_TEXT);
    outtextxy(midx/2,midy/3,"After restoring
    default values");
    settextstyle(1,0,4);
    outtextxy(midx-75,10,"LINE STYLE SETTINGS");
    return ;
}

/* Image size */

image_size_fun()
{
    cleardevice();
    buffer = (char*) malloc(10000);
    circle(midx/2,midy/2,midy/4);
    size = imagesize(midx-100,midy-100,
    midx+100,midy+100);
    getimage(midx-100,midy-100,
    midx+100,midy+100,buffer);
    settextstyle(1,0,4);
    outtextxy(midx-75,10,"Catch & Place With Size");
    freemem(buffer);
    press_key();
    init();
    cleardevice();
    buffer = (char*) malloc(10000);
    circle(midx/2,midy/2,midy/4);
    size = imagesize(midx-100,midy-100,
    midx+100,midy+100);
    getimage(midx-100,midy-100,
    midx+100,midy+100,buffer);
    putimage(midx+75,midy+75,buffer,XOR_PUT);
    freemem(buffer);
    settextstyle(1,0,4);
    outtextxy(midx-75,10,"Placed With Size of
    Image");
    return ;
}

/* Install user fonts */

user_font_fun()
{
```

(Contd.)

```
    /* 20 fonts can be installed at one time */

    cleardevice();
    userfont = installuserfont("USER.CHR");
    settextstyle(userfont, HORIZ_DIR,4);
    outtextxy(midx,midy,"FONT SETTING IS DONE");
    settextstyle(1,0,4);
    outtextxy(midx-75,10,"FONT SETTING");
    return ;
}

/* Line relative function */

line_rel_fun()
{
    cleardevice();
    moveto(getmaxx()/4,getmaxy()/4); /* set the
    corner */
    sprintf(msg,"<--( %d, %d ) is the here
    1",getx(), gety());

    /* Display the information */

    ht = textheight("W");
    settextjustify(CENTER_TEXT,CENTER_TEXT);
    outtextxy(midx/2,midy/2,msg);
    press_key();
    init();
    moveto(getmaxx()/4,getmaxy()/4); /* set the
    corner */
    sprintf(msg,"<--( %d, %d ) is the here
    1",getx(), gety());

    /* Display the information */

    ht = textheight("W");
    settextjustify(CENTER_TEXT,CENTER_TEXT);
    outtextxy(midx/2,midy/2,msg);
    linerel(midx/2,midy-10); /* from starting point
    to starting point value + this point value */

    sprintf(msg,"<--( %d, %d ) is the here 2
    ",getx(), gety());
```

(Contd.)

```
    ht = textheight("W");
    settextjustify(CENTER_TEXT,CENTER_TEXT);
    outtext(msg);
    settextstyle(1,0,4);
    outtextxy(midx-75,10,"RELATIVE LINE ");
    return ;

}

/* Motion relative to previous poit */

mov_fun()
{
    cleardevice() ;
    moveto(midx/2,midy/4);
    putpixel(getx(),gety(),RED);
                        /* write pixel of red color*/
    sprintf(msg,"<--( %d, %d ) is the here
    ",getx(), gety());
    ht = textheight("W");
    settextjustify(CENTER_TEXT,CENTER_TEXT);
    outtextxy(midx/2+5,midy/4,msg);
    settextstyle(1,0,4);
    outtextxy(midx-75,10,"RELATIVE MOVE ");
    press_key();
    init();
    moveto(midx/2,midy/4);
    putpixel(getx(),gety(),RED);
                         /* write pixel ofred color*/
    sprintf(msg,"<--( %d, %d ) is the here
    ",getx(), gety());
    ht = textheight("W");
    settextjustify(CENTER_TEXT,CENTER_TEXT);
    outtextxy(midx/2+5,midy/4,msg);
    moverel(midx+50,midy+50);
    putpixel(getx(),gety(),RED);
    sprintf(msg,"<--( %d, %d ) is the here
    ",getx(), gety());
    ht = textheight("W");
    settextjustify(CENTER_TEXT,CENTER_TEXT);
    outtext(msg);
    settextstyle(1,0,4);
```

(Contd.)

```
    outtextxy(midx-75,10,"RELATIVE MOVE ");
    return ;
}

/*  The outtext function */

output_fun()
{
    /* This is function which is used to write text
       in graphics mode on  the screen */

    cleardevice();
    moveto(midx,midy);
    outtext("THIS ");
    outtext("IS ");
    outtext("TIME ");
    outtext("TO  ");
    outtext("ENJOY");
    settextstyle(1,0,4);
    outtextxy(midx-75,10,"OUTPUT FUN outtext() ");
    return ;
}

/* Tells about pieslice */

pie_fun()
{
    cleardevice() ;
    pieslice(midx,midy,stangle,endangle, radius);
    settextstyle(1,0,4);
    outtextxy(midx-75,10,"PIE CHART ");
    return ;
}

/* Restore function */

rest_fun()
{
    cleardevice() ;
    ht = textheight("W");
    settextjustify(CENTER_TEXT,CENTER_TEXT);
    outtextxy(midx,midy,"Press a key to exit from
    graphics mode  ");
```

(Contd.)

```
    press_key();
    init();
    cleardevice() ;
    ht = textheight("W");
    settextjustify(CENTER_TEXT,CENTER_TEXT);
    outtextxy(midx,midy,"Press a key to exit from
    graphics mode  ");
    restorecrtmode();
    ht = textheight("W");
    settextjustify(CENTER_TEXT,CENTER_TEXT);
    outtextxy(midx,midy+ht,"We are in text mode now
    ");
    outtextxy(midx,midy+ht*2,"Press a key to go
    back in graphics mode");
    setgraphmode(getgraphmode());
    ht = textheight("W");
    settextjustify(CENTER_TEXT,CENTER_TEXT);
    outtextxy(midx,midy+ht*4,"We are in graphics
    mode now ");
    outtextxy(midx,midy+ht*6,"Press a key ");
    settextstyle(1,0,4);
    outtextxy(midx-75,10,"MODE SETTINGS ");
    return ;
}

/* The sector function */

sector_fun()
{
    for(i = EMPTY_FILL ; i <= USER_FILL; i++ )
    {
      setfillstyle(i,getmaxcolor());
      sector(midx,midy,45,135,30,50);
      settextstyle(1,0,4);
      outtextxy(midx-75,10,"SECTOR ");
      press_key();
      init();
    }
    return ;
}

/* The fill pattern */
```

(Contd.)

```
fill_pattern_fun()
{
    settextstyle(1,0,4);
    outtextxy(midx-75,10,"WEL COME ON ");
    outtextxy(midx-75,30,"FILL PATTERN DEMO");
    press_key();
    init() ;
    for(i = EMPTY_FILL ; i <= USER_FILL; i++ )
    {
      setfillstyle(i,getmaxcolor());
      pieslice(midx/4,midy/4,stangle,endangle,
      radius/4);
      sector(midx,midy,45,135,30,50);
      settextstyle(1,0,4);
      outtextxy(midx-75,10,f_name[i]);
      press_key();
      init();
    }
    return ;
}

/* The default setting function */

int huge detectEGA()
{
    int driver , graphmode,sugmode = 0;
    detectgraph(&driver,&graphmode);

    if(( driver == EGA) || ( driver == VGA ))
      return (sugmode) ;
    else
      return grError ;
}

/*  Resetting of graphics mode */

/* Graphics error checking  function */

void  checkerrors()
{
    int error_code ;
    int midx,midy;
    midx = getmaxx()/2 ;
```

(Contd.)

```
    midy = getmaxy()/2 ;

    error_code = graphresult();
    if( error_code != grOk )
    {

    outtextxy(midx,midy,grapherrormsg(error_code));
    outtextxy(midx/2,midy/3,"Press A key ");
    exit(1) ;
    }
    return ;
}

/* Resetting of graphics device driver */

driver_set_fun()
{

    /* install a user written device driver */

    cleardevice();
    init();
    installuserdriver("EGA", detectEGA);
    gd = DETECT ; /* must force dectection routine */
    initgraph(&gd,&gm,"c:\\backup\\tc");
    checkerrors() ; /* check errors during graphics
      driver installation */
    line(0,0,100,100);
    lineto(midx*2,midy*2);
    return ;
}

/** The color function */

col_fun()
{
    settextstyle(1,0,4);
    outtextxy(midx-75,10,"FIRST BLACK PRESS A KEY
");
    for ( i = BLACK ; i <= WHITE ; i++ )
    {
      setcolor(i);
      circle(midx,midy,midy/3);
```

(Contd.)

```
      settextstyle(1,0,4);
      outtextxy(midx-75,10,color_name1[i]);
      press_key() ;
      init();
    }
    return ;
}

/* EGA  color function */

ega_col_fun()
{
    int j ;
    j = 0 ;

    settextstyle(1,0,4);
    outtextxy(midx-75,10,"EGA FIRST BLACK PRESS A
    KEY ");
    for ( i = EGA_BLACK ; i <= EGA_LIGHTGRAY ; i++
)
    {
      if ( j == 6 )
      {
        cleardevice();
        j = 20 ;
        setcolor(j);
        circle(midx,midy,midy/3);
        settextstyle(1,0,4);
        outtextxy(midx-75,10,ega_color_name1[6]);
        press_key() ;
        init();
      }
      if ( j == 20 )
      {
        j = 7 ;
        cleardevice();
        setcolor(j);
        circle(midx,midy,midy/3);
        settextstyle(1,0,4);
        outtextxy(midx-75,10,ega_color_name1[j]);
        press_key();
        init();
      }
```

(Contd.)

```
      setcolor(i);
      circle(midx,midy,midy/3);
      settextstyle(1,0,4);
      outtextxy(midx-75,10,ega_color_name1[j]);
      j++;
      press_key() ;
      init();
    }
   return ;
}

/* Light EGA color function */

light_col_fun()
{
    int j ;
    j = 0 ;
    for ( i = EGA_DARKGRAY ; i <= EGA_WHITE  ; i++
)
    {
      setcolor(i);
      circle(midx,midy,midy/3);
      settextstyle(1,0,4);
      outtextxy(midx-75,10,light_color_name2[j]);
      j++;
      press_key() ;
      init();
    }
    return ;
}

/* CGA  color function */

cga_col_fun()
{
    int k ;
    int j = 0 ;
    for( k = 1 ;k <= 4 ; k++ ) /* palette color */
    {
      for ( i = 1 ; i <= 3 ; i++ )
      {
        setpalette(i,k);        /* set the palette */
        setcolor(i);
```

(Contd.)

```
        circle(midx,midy,midy/3);
        settextstyle(1,0,4);
        outtextxy(midx-75,10,cga_color_name1[j]);
        j++ ;

        press_key() ;
        init();
      }
    }
    return ;
}

/* Function to control the key */

press_key()
{
    textcolor(RED|BLINK);
    gotoxy(60,23);
    outtextxy(midx-120,midy+120," Press a Key ");
    getch();
    closegraph();
    return ;
}

/* The init function to change from text mode to
graphics mode */

init()
{
    detectgraph(&gd,&gm);
    initgraph(&gd,&gm,"\\backpup\\tc");
    checkerrors() ;
    midx = getmaxx()/2 ;
      /* Gives size of screen in graphics mode */
    midy = getmaxy()/2 ;
    /* Like 640x480 pixels here we have divide it by
        2*/
    setcolor(RED);              /* Set the drawing */

    cleardevice();
    setcolor(RED);
    return ;
}
/* Line style function */
```

(Contd.)

```
line_style_fun()
{
    for ( i = SOLID_LINE ; i <= USERBIT_LINE; i++)
    {
      setlinestyle(i,1,NORM_WIDTH);
      line(0,0,midx,midy);
      settextstyle(1,0,4);
      outtextxy(midx-75,10,line_name[i]);
      settextstyle(1,0,4);
      outtextxy(midx-75,30,"NORM  LINE");
      press_key();
      init();

      setlinestyle(i,1,THICK_WIDTH);
      line(0,0,midx,midy);
      settextstyle(1,0,4);
      outtextxy(midx-75,10,line_name[i]);
      settextstyle(1,0,4);
      outtextxy(midx-75,30,"THICK LINE");
      press_key();
      init();
    }
    return ;
}

/* Choice function */

choice_fun()
{
    int ch ;
    clrscr();
    textcolor(RED|BLINK);
    gotoxy(20,23);
    textcolor(RED|BLINK);
    printf("\n Enter Your Choice from 0 to 40 ,0 TO
EXIT: ");
    scanf("%d",&ch);
    return(ch);
}
```

Program 13.

```
// GRMATH.C
/*******************************************/
/*        Plot function y = x ^ 2 /5 +1    */
/*     graphical equivalent of graphtxt.c  */
/*******************************************/

# include<conio.h>
# include<stdio.h>
# include<math.h>
# include<graphics.h>

 void  checkerrors();

/* Global variables */

   int midx,midy;
   int gd,gm;

  void main()
      {
       float  x;
       float y;
       int i, j;

       clrscr();
       init();
      moveto(5,5);
       for( x = 5; x < 40 ; x++)
          {
     y = pow(x,2)/5 +1 + 0.5;
     lineto(x,y);
     circle(x,y,2);
          }

        line(5,5,midx,5);
        outtextxy(midx+10,5,"X-axis");
        line(5,5,5,midy+100);
        outtextxy(5,midy+100," Y-axis");
        outtextxy(midx-150,midy-50,"<==== y = x^2/
```

(Contd.)

```
5 +1 ");
        outtextxy(midx,midy+50," Press a Key ");
        getch();
        closegraph();
        }

  /* init function to change from text mode */
  /*  to graphics mode                      */

 init()
  {
    detectgraph(&gd,&gm);
    initgraph(&gd,&gm,"\\tc");
    checkerrors() ;
    midx = getmaxx()/2 ;
        /* gives size of screenin graphics mode */
    midy = getmaxy()/2 ;
        /* like 640x480 pixels here we have divide
           it by 2*/
    setcolor(RED);            /* set the drawing */

    cleardevice();
    setcolor(RED);
      return ;
   }

/* Graphics error checking  function */

void  checkerrors()
   {
   int error_code ;
   int midx,midy;
   midx = getmaxx()/2 ;
   midy = getmaxy()/2 ;

   error_code = graphresult();
   if( error_code != grOk )
     {
   outtextxy(midx,midy,grapherrormsg(error_code));
     outtextxy(midx/2,midy/3,"Press A key ");
     exit(1) ;
```

(Contd.)

```
    }
    return ;
  }
```

Program 14.

```
/* icon.c */

# include<stdio.h>
# include<dos.h>
# include<conio.h>
# include<bios.h>
# include<string.h>

# define TURBOC
# define IY 144
# define IX 240
# define XDIM 40
# define YDIM 32
# define XPAND 3

# define BCK_GND 9
# define FORE_GND 15
# define HIGHLIGHT 13

struct icon_type
    {
      unsigned image[XDIM][YDIM]; /* icon image */
      void (*func)(); /* pointer to function
associated with each icon */
      int x, y; /* x, y coordinate */
    } icon;

   char far *egabase;
/*******************************************/
                     int index;
                       int val;
/*******************************************/
# define ENABLE 0x0F
# define INDEXREG 0x3CE
# define VALREG 0x3CF

# ifdef TURBOC
```

(Contd.)

```
# define OUTINDEX(index, val) outp ((INDEXREG),
(index));\
        outp((VALREG), (val));

# endif

# ifdef MICROSOFTC
# define OUTINDEX(index, val) outp ((INDEXREG),
(index));\
        outp((VALREG), (val));
# endif

# define WIDTH 80L

/* These range values assume EGA mode 16 */

# define XMAX 639
# define YMAX 349
# define XMIN 0
# define YMIN 0

void putpoint (int x, int y, int color, int how)
  {
  register unsigned char mask = 0x80;
  register char far *base;
  unsigned dummy;

  base = (char far *) (egabase + ((long) y*WIDTH
+(long) x/8L));
  mask >>= x %8;
  dummy = *base ;

  OUTINDEX(0, color);
  OUTINDEX(1, ENABLE);
  OUTINDEX(3, how);
  OUTINDEX(8, mask);

  *base = 1;

  OUTINDEX(0, 0);
  OUTINDEX(1, 0);
  OUTINDEX(3, 0);
  OUTINDEX(8, 0xFF);
```

(Contd.)

```
    }

 void set_mode( int mode_code)
   {
      union REGS reg;
      reg.h.al = mode_code;
      reg.h.ah = 0;
      int86(0x10, &reg, &reg);
   }

 char getpoint( int x, int y)
   {
      union REGS reg;

      reg.h.ah = 13;
      reg.x.dx = y;
      reg.x.cx = x;
      reg.h.bh = 0;
      int86(16, &reg, &reg);
      return (reg.h.al);
   }

 void clrscr()
   {
      union REGS reg;

      reg.h.ah = 7;
      reg.h.al = 0;  /* clear the screen */
      reg.h.ch = 0;  /* upper left row */
      reg.h.cl = 0;  /* upper left column */
      reg.h.dh = 24; /* lower right row */
      reg.h.dl = 79; /* lower left column */
      reg.h.bh = 0;  /* use page 0 */

      int86(0x10, &reg, &reg);
   }

 void gotoxy(int x, int y)
   {
      union REGS reg;
      reg.h.ah = 2;  /* cursor addressing function
*/
      reg.h.dl = x;  /* column coordinate */
```

(Contd.)

```
    reg.h.dh = y;  /* row coordinate */
    reg.h.bh = 0;  /* video page */

    int86(0x10, &reg, &reg);
  }
  /* clears at the end of the line */
  void clr_eol(int x, int y)
    {
   for(; x < 80; x++)
    {
      gotoxy(x, y);
      printf(" ");
    }
   }

/* display the expanded grid */

void display_grid()
 {
   register int x, y;
   for(y = IY;y < (IY+YDIM); y++)
   putpoint(x+((x-IX)*XPAND), y+((y-IY)*XPAND),
icon.image[x-IX][y-IY], 0);
 }

/* Display the icon */

 void display_icon(int startx, int starty)
  {
   register int x, y;

   for (y = starty; y < starty +YDIM; y++)
      for (x = startx; x < startx +XDIM; x++)
     putpoint(x, y, icon.image[x-startx][y-
starty], 0);
  }

  /* Initialize the icon */
  void init_icon()
  {
   register int x, y;
    for (x = 0; x < XDIM; x++)
     for (y = 0; y < YDIM; y++)
```

(Contd.)

```
        icon.image[x][y] = BCK_GND;
    }

/* getkey() function return code of the scan key */

    char getkey()
     {
      union key
        {
          int i;
          char ch[2];
        } k;

    # ifdef TURBOC
    k.i = bioskey(0);
    # endif

    # ifdef MICROSOFTC
       k.i = _bios_keybrd(0);
    # endif
    return (k.ch[1]);
  }

 /* edit icon */
 void edit_icon()
  {
    register int x, y;
    char ch, pen, temp;
    char file[80];

    x = IX; /* set x to upper left corner */
    y = IY; /* set y to upper left corner */

    pen =  BCK_GND;

    display_icon(0, IY);
    display_grid();

    do
    {
      /* write pixel to grid */
      putpoint(x+((x-IX)*XPAND), y+((y-IY)*XPAND),
      pen, 0);
```

(Contd.)

```
  /* save pixel to icon */
  putpoint(x-IX, y, icon.image[x-IX][y-IY], 0);
  getpoint(x+((x-IX)*XPAND), y+((y-IY)*XPAND));
  putpoint(x+((x-IX)*XPAND), y+((y-IY)*XPAND),
  HIGHLIGHT, 0);

  ch = getkey();

  putpoint(x+((x-IX)*XPAND), y+((y-IY)*XPAND),
  temp, 0);

switch(ch)
{
  case 75: /* left */
    x--;
    break;
  case 77: /* right */
    x++;
    break;
  case 72: /* up */
    y--;
    break;
  case 80: /* down */
    y++;
    break;

  case 71: /* up left */
    x--;
    y--;
    break;

  case 73: /* up right */
    x++;
    y--;
    break;

  case 79: /* down left */
    x--;
    y++;
    break;

  case 81: /* down right */
    x++;
```

(Contd.)

```
        y++;
        break;

      case 59: pen = FORE_GND; /* F1 -> pen down */
        break;

      case 60: pen = BCK_GND; /* F2 -> pen up */
        break;

      case 61: save_icon();
        break;

      case 62: load_icon("");
        display_icon(0, IY);
        display_grid();
        break;

      case 63: init_icon();
        display_icon(0, IY);
        display_grid();
        break;
        }

        if(x < IX)
      x++;
      if (x > IX+XDIM-1)
        x--;

        if(y < IY)
      y++;
      if (y > IY+YDIM-1)
        y--;

    } while(ch != 64);
      }

/* save icon */
save_icon()
 {
 FILE *fp;
 char file[80];
 int result;
```

(Contd.)

```
gotoxy(0, 22);
printf("\n Save to: ");
gets(file);

fp = fopen (file, "wb");

if (fp == NULL)
 {
  printf("\n File open error: %s", file);
  perror("Error: ");
  return 0;
 }
  fwrite(&icon, sizeof(icon), 1, fp);

  if (ferror(fp))
result = 0;
fclose (fp);
clr_eol(0,22);
return (result);
 }

/* load icon */
 load_icon(char *name)
 {
 FILE *fp;
 char file[80];
 int result;

 if(!*name)
  {
     gotoxy(0,22);
     printf("\n Load from: ");
     gets(file);
  }
  else
   strcpy(file, name);

   fp = fopen(file, "rb");
   if (fp == NULL)
      {
  printf("\n File open error: %s", file);
  perror("Error: ");
  return (0);
```

(Contd.)

```
    }

    fread (&icon, sizeof(icon), 1, fp);
    if(ferror(fp))
     result = 0;
     else
         result = 1;
     fclose(fp);
     clr_eol(0, 22);
     return(result);
    }

void main(int argc, char *argv[])
 {
   set_mode (16);
   /* initialize the pointer to the EGA/VGA  video
      RAM */

   # ifdef TURBOC
   egabase = (char far *) MK_FP (0xA000, 0000);
   # endif

   # ifdef MICROSOFTC
   egabase = (char far *) 0xA0000000;
   # endif
   printf("\n F1: pen down F2: pen up F3: save
   icon");
   printf("\n F4: load icon F5: erase F6: quit");
   init_icon();
   if(argc == 2 )
   load_icon(argv[1]);
   edit_icon();
   set_mode(2);
    }
```

Program 15.

```
/* image.c */

/* bouncing ball created from bit image */
```

(Contd.)

```
#include <graphics.h>
#include <conio.h>
#define LEFT     0
#define TOP      0
#define RIGHT   400
#define BOTTOM  349
#define RADIUS   20

void main(void)
{
   int driver, mode;
   int x, y, dx, dy, oldx, oldy;
   unsigned char ballbuff[2000];

   driver = DETECT;

   initgraph(&driver, &mode, "c:\\backup\\tc");

   rectangle(LEFT, TOP, RIGHT, BOTTOM);

   x = LEFT + RADIUS + 10;
   y = TOP  + RADIUS + 10;
   setcolor(LIGHTGREEN);
   setfillstyle(SOLID_FILL, LIGHTGREEN);
   circle(x, y, RADIUS);
   floodfill(x, y, LIGHTGREEN);
   /* place image in memory */
   getimage(x-RADIUS, y-RADIUS, x+RADIUS,
   y+RADIUS, ballbuff);
   dx = 2;                   /* set speed of ball */
   dy = 2;
   while ( !kbhit() )         /* exit on keypress */
   {                          /* memory image to
                                 screen */
    putimage(x-RADIUS, y-RADIUS, ballbuff,
    COPY_PUT);
    oldx = x;
    oldy = y;            /* remember where it was */
    x += dx;
    y += dy;             /* move its coordinates */
    /* reflect it at edges */
    if( x<=LEFT+RADIUS+2 || x>=RIGHT-RADIUS-2 )
      dx = -dx;
```

(Contd.)

```
    if( y<=TOP+RADIUS+2 || y>=BOTTOM-RADIUS-2 )
      dy = -dy;
    /* erase old image */
    putimage(oldx-RADIUS, oldy-RADIUS, ballbuff,
    XOR_PUT);
   }
   closegraph();
}
```

Program 16.

```
/* mandel.c */

/* generates the mandelbrot set */

#include <graphics.h>  /* for graphics functions */
#include <conio.h>     /* for kbhit(), getch() */
#include <process.h>   /* for exit() */
#define XMAX 400       /* change these to change
                          size */
#define YMAX 250       /*    of picture */
#define MAXCOUNT 16    /* number of iterations */

void main(void)
{
   int x, y;                /* location of pixel on
                               screen */
   float xscale, yscale;
                         /* distance between pixels */
   float left, top;
                     /* location of top left corner */
   float xside, yside;
                                /* length of sides */
   float zx, zy;
                          /* real and imag parts of z */
   float cx, cy;
                          /* real and imag parts of c */
   float tempx;
                               /* briefly holds zx */
   int count;
                             /* number of iterations */
   int driver, mode;
```

(Contd.)

```
                        /* graphics driver and mode */

left = -2.0;
                        /* coordinates for entire */
top = 1.25;
                        /* mandelbrot set */
xside = 2.5;
                        /* change to see details */
yside = -2.5;
                        /* of set */
xscale = xside / XMAX;
                        /* set scale factors */
yscale = yside / YMAX;
driver = DETECT;
                        /* auto detect */
initgraph(&driver, &mode, "\\tc\\bgi" );
                        /* initialize */
rectangle( 0, 0, XMAX+1, YMAX+1 );
                        /* border */

for(y=1; y<=YMAX; y++)
                        /* for each pixel column */
{
  for(x=1; x<=XMAX; x++)
                        /* for each pixel row */
  {
    cx = x*xscale+left;
                        /* set c to pixel location */
    cy = y*yscale+top;
    zx = zy = 0;
                        /* set z = 0 */
    count = 0;
                        /* reset count */

                        /* size of z < 2 */

    while( zx*zx+zy*zy<4 && count<MAXCOUNT )
    {
      tempx = zx*zx - zy*zy + cx;  /* set z =
      z*z + c */
      zy = 2*zx*zy + cy;
      zx = tempx;
      count++;              /* another iteration */
```

(Contd.)

```
        }
        putpixel(x, y, count); /* color is count */

        if( kbhit() )          /* to abort program */
          exit(0);     /* before picture finished */
      } /* end for(x) */
    } /* end for(y) */
    getch();
    closegraph();
}
```

Program 17.

```
/* model.c */

# include<stdio.h>
# include<conio.h>
# include<io.h>
# include<dos.h>

# define VIDEO 0X10
# define SETMODE 0

void set_mode( int mode_code)
  {
     union REGS reg;
     reg.h.al = mode_code;
     reg.h.ah = SETMODE;
     int86(VIDEO, &reg, &reg);
  }

 void main()
 {
     int mod;
     printf("\n Input the mode value: ");
     scanf("%d", &mod);
     set_mode(mod);
```

Program 18.

```
/* MOVE.C */
/
/***********************************************/
/* Gives the demo of some text mode function   */
/* which will work like graphics function in 'C'*/
/* display character V at the screen and which made*/
/* from character v and WELCOME word display in it*/
/* when we press a key a portion cut and paste  */
/* operation performed and message cut-paste is */
/* display with blinking                        */
/***********************************************/

# include<stdio.h>
# include<conio.h>
# include<io.h>

 void main()
     {
      register int i;
      register int j;
      textmode(80);  /* text mode 80 column */
      clrscr();

 /* Produce character V on the screen */

      for( i = 1, j = 1 ; j < 24; i++ , j++)
     {
      gotoxy(i,j);
      cprintf("v");
      }

      for(i = i , j = j ; j > 0; i++, j--)
       {
        gotoxy(i,j);
        cprintf("v");
       }
    /* Back ground color setting */

      textbackground(LIGHTBLUE);
      textcolor(RED);            /* Set text color */
```

(Contd.)

```
gotoxy(20,12);
textcolor(GREEN | BLINK );
                /* Set text color with blink */

textbackground( BLACK);
                    /* Set back ground color */
cprintf("WELCOME ") ;
getch();
movetext(20,20,28,24,20,1);   /* Move text */
gotoxy(20,6);
cprintf("cut paste");
getch();
textmode(LASTMODE);
                /* Last mode of the screen */
}
```

Program 19.

```
/* plot.c */

#include <graphics.h>
#include <conio.h>
#include <math.h>

void main(void)
   {
   int driver, mode;
   double angle, cosofA;  // angle and sin of angle
   int x, y;              // screen coordinates

   driver = DETECT;

   initgraph(&driver, &mode, "c:\\tc\\bgi");
   line(100, 120, 400, 120);    /* line along x-
   axis */
   for(x=100; x<360; x++)
      {
      angle = ((double)x / 200) * (2 * 3.14159265);
      cosofA = cos(angle);
      y = 120 - 100*cosofA;
      putpixel(x, y, GREEN);
      }
```

(Contd.)

```
    outtextxy(200,200, "cos(theta)");
  getch();
  closegraph();
  }
```

Program 20.

```
/* putpoint.c */

# include<stdio.h>
# include<conio.h>
# include<io.h>
# include<dos.h>

void putpoint(int x, int y, int color)
  {
     union REGS reg;

     reg.h.bh = 0;
     reg.h.ah = 12;
     reg.h.al = color;
     reg.x.dx = y;
     reg.x.cx = x;
     int86(16, &reg, &reg);
  }

 void main()
 {
     int x, y;
     int color;
     /*
     printf("\n Input the values of x and y: ");
     scanf("%d%d", &x, &y);
     printf("\n Input the color of the pixel: ");
     scanf("%d", &color);
     */
     clrscr();
     for(x=0; x<80; x++)
     for(y =0; y<25; y++)
     putpoint(x,y, y);
     getch();
  }
```

Program 21.

```
/* random.c                                                        */
/* generate random number rectangles                               */
/* generate random number circles                                  */
/* generate random number text size of text welcome                */
/* generate random number colors for above
information */

# include<graphics.h>
# include<dos.h>
# include<stdlib.h>
# include<conio.h>

void main()
    {
    int gd = DETECT ;
    int gm ;
    int num ,i;
    int x1, y1, x2, y2 ;

    initgraph(&gd, &gm,"c:\\backup\\tc");

    for(i =100 ; i< getmaxy(); i++)
    {
    cleardevice();

    x1 = random(i) ;     /* random value of x1 */
    y1 = random(i+10) ;  /* random value of y1 */
    x2 = random(i+20) ;  /* random value of x2 */
    y2 = random(i+30) ;  /* random value of y2 */
    setcolor(x1);
   rectangle(x1+100,y1+100,x2+100,y2+100);

 /*  Sound section */

    sound(x1);
    sound(y1);
    sound(x2);
    sound(y2);
    delay(100);
```

(Contd.)

```
/* End of sound section */

      nosound();
      settextstyle(x1,0,y1);
      outtextxy(x1,y1, "WELCOME");
      circle(getmaxx()/2,getmaxy()/2,x1);
      delay(1000);

      }

      }
```

Program 22.

```
/* SOUND.C */
/*******************************************/
/* Generate random number of circles       */
/* from different corners as well as from center*/
/* a stream of circles of different size at the */
/* center moving upward continuously how many   */
/* circles formed depends on the type of monitor*/
/* and mode used                                */
/*******************************************/

# include<graphics.h>
# include<dos.h>
# include<stdlib.h>
# include<conio.h>

void main()
      {
      int gd = DETECT ;
      int gm ;
      int num ,i,j ;
      initgraph(&gd, &gm,"C:\\tc\\bgi");
      j = 0;
      while(!kbhit())
      {
      for(i =1 ; i< getmaxy()/2; i++)
      {
      delay(100);
      num = random(i);        /* random number  */
```

(Contd.)

```
sound(500+num);
circle(1,1,num);
circle(getmaxx()-1,1,num);
circle(1,getmaxy()-1,num);
circle(getmaxx()-1,getmaxy()-1,num);
circle(getmaxx()/2,getmaxy()/2,num/4);
setcolor(j);
j++;
if ( j == 128 )
j = 0;
}
nosound();
}
}
```

Program 23.

```
/* square.c */
/* draws set of squares and demonstrates relative
motion */

#include <graphics.h>
#include <conio.h>
#define MAX   320
#define GRID   50
#define SIDE   46

void square(int side);

void main(void)
  {
  int driver, mode;
  int x, y;
  driver = DETECT;

  initgraph(&driver, &mode, "c:\\tc\\bgi");
  for(y=10; y<MAX; y+=GRID)   /* move down rows */
     for(x=10; x<MAX; x+=GRID)
           /* move across columns */
    {
    moveto(x, y);     /* move current position  */
    square(SIDE);        /* draw a square there */
```

(Contd.)

```
  }
getch();
closegraph();
 }

/* square() function to make square */

void square(int side)
  {
  linerel(side, 0); /* top, left to right */
  linerel(0, side); /* right side, top to bottom*/
  linerel(-side, 0); /* bottom, right to left */
  linerel(0, -side);/ *left side, bottom to top */
  }
```

Program 24.

```
/* viewport.c */
/* draws circle and line within viewport */

#include <graphics.h>
#include <conio.h>

void main(void)
  {
  int driver, mode;
  int left=0, top=0, right=250, bot=175;
                     /* viewport */
  int clip=1;       /* viewport clipping enabled */
  int x1=0, y1=0;
  int x2=349, y2=349;
  int xC=175, yC=175;
  int radius=150;

  driver = DETECT;                    /* auto detect*/
                         /* initialize graphics */
  initgraph(&driver, &mode, "c:\\tc\\bgi");

   outtextxy(200,350," Drawing line and circle
   before creating a viewport ");
  rectangle(left, top, right, bot);
  line(x1, y1, x2, y2);
  circle(xC, yC, radius);
```

(Contd.)

```
    outtextxy(200, 370,"Press a key");
    getch();
    clearviewport();
    outtextxy(200,350," Drawing line and circle
     after creating a viewport ");
    setviewport(left, top, right, bot, clip);
                        /* set viewport dimensions */

    rectangle(left, top, right, bot);
                     /* draw rectangle on viewport */
    line(x1, y1, x2, y2);
    circle(xC, yC, radius);
    outtextxy(100, 70,"Press a key");
    getch();
    closegraph();
    }
```

Program 25.

```
/* vonkoch.c */

# include<stdio.h>
# include<graphics.h>
# include<conio.h>
# include<math.h>
# include<ctype.h>

/* factor is set to sqrt(3)/2 by graph_vonkoch and
is used by vonkoch */
double factor;

char inbuff[80]; /* for user input */
void vonkoch(int level, int mscale, int rot);
void graph_vonkoch();

/* function main() */
 main()
  {
    for(;;)
      {  printf("Do another y = yes and n = no)?
  ");
    gets(inbuff);
```

(Contd.)

```
    if (toupper(*inbuff) != 'Y')
    return ;
        graph_vonkoch();
      }
  }

  /* graph vonkoch */

 void graph_vonkoch()
    {
   int gdriver = DETECT, gmode, errorcode, level;
   printf("Input level: ");
   gets(inbuff);
   level = atoi(inbuff);
   initgraph(&gdriver, &gmode, "c:\\tc\bgi");
   errorcode = graphresult();
   if(errorcode != 0)
    {
      printf("Graphics error: %s",
       grapherrormsg(errorcode));
      return ;
   }
   factor = sqrt(3)/2;
   moveto(0,0);

   /* draw snowflake
   level = user- specified level*/
   vonkoch(level, getmaxx(), 0);

   outtextxy(0, getmaxy()/2, "Press any key to
   continue");
   getch();
   closegraph();
     }

    void vonkoch(int level, int scale, int rot)
       {
    if(level ==0)
     switch(rot)
     {
       case 0 : linerel(scale, 0);
       return;
```

(Contd.)

```
        case 1 : linerel(scale/2, scale*factor);
        return;
        case 2: linerel(-scale/2, scale*factor);
        return;
        case 3: linerel(-scale, 0);
        return;
        case 4: linerel(-scale/2, -scale*factor);
        return;
        case 5: linerel(scale/2, -scale*factor);
        return;
        }
        vonkoch(level-1, scale/3, rot);
        vonkoch(level-1, scale/3, (rot + 1) %6);
        vonkoch(level-1, scale/3, (rot + 5) %6);
        vonkoch(level-1, scale/3, rot);
        vonkoch(level-1, scale/3, rot);
    }
```

Program 26.

```
/* vonkoch1.c */

# include<stdio.h>
# include<graphics.h>
# include<conio.h>
# include<math.h>
# include<ctype.h>

/* factor is set to sqrt(3)/2 by graph_vonkoch and
is used by vonkoch */
double factor;

char inbuff[80]; /* for user input */
void vonkoch(int level, int mscale, int rot);
void graph_vonkoch();

/* function main() */
main()
  {
    for(;;)
      {  printf("Do another y = yes and n = no)?
");
```

(Contd.)

```
   gets(inbuff);
    if (toupper(*inbuff) != 'Y')
    return ;
       graph_vonkoch();
      }
  }

 /* graph vonkoch */

void graph_vonkoch()
   {
  int gdriver = DETECT, gmode, errorcode, level;
  printf("Input level: ");
  gets(inbuff);
  level = atoi(inbuff);
  initgraph(&gdriver, &gmode, "c:\\tc\bgi");
  errorcode = graphresult();
  if(errorcode != 0)
   {
     printf("Graphics error: %s",
     grapherrormsg(errorcode));
     return ;
  }
  factor = sqrt(3)/2;
  moveto(getmaxx(), getmaxy()/2);

  /* draw snowflake
  level = user- specified level*/
  vonkoch(level, getmaxx(), 3);

  outtextxy(0, 0, "Press any key to continue");
  getch();
  closegraph();
    }

   void vonkoch(int level, int scale, int rot)
       {
   if(level ==0)
    switch(rot)
    {
      case 0 : linerel(scale, 0);
      return;
```

(Contd.)

```
        case 1 : linerel(scale/2, scale*factor);
        return;
        case 2: linerel(-scale/2, scale*factor);
        return;
        case 3: linerel(-scale, 0);
        return;
        case 4: linerel(-scale/2, -scale*factor);
        return;
        case 5: linerel(scale/2, -scale*factor);
        return;
        }
        vonkoch(level-1, scale/3, rot);
        vonkoch(level-1, scale/3, (rot + 1) %6);
        vonkoch(level-1, scale/3, (rot + 5) %6);
        vonkoch(level-1, scale/3, rot);
        vonkoch(level-1, scale/3, rot);
}
```

Program 27.

```
/* WINDOWTX.C */
/* Window program */

# include<stdio.h>
# include<conio.h>

  int left ;
  int top ;
  int right ;
  int bottom ;

  int color  = WHITE ;

  void box_draw( int , int , int , int , int ) ;
                                        /* Prototype */

    void main()
    {
      clrscr();

      left   = 5 ;
      top    = 2;
```

(Contd.)

```
    right  = 55 ;
    bottom = 20 ;

  box_draw(left,top,right,bottom,RED);

   left   = 25 ;
   top    = 6;
   right  = 55 ;
   bottom = 18 ;

  box_draw(left,top,right , bottom,YELLOW);

   left   = 56 ;
   top    = 13;
   right  = 78 ;
   bottom = 24 ;

  box_draw(left,top,right , bottom,YELLOW);

   }

/* Function definition */

  void box_draw(int left, int top, int right, int
bottom ,int color )
     {
      int i ;
      int width ;
      int hight;
      char *string[] ={
          "MONDAY","TUESDAY",
          "WEDNESDAY","THURSDAY",
          "FRIDAY","SATURDAY",
          "SUNDAY"
          } ;
       width = right - left + 1 ;
       hight = bottom - top + 1 ;
      window(left, top, right, bottom+1);
      textcolor(color);
      for( i = 1 ; i <= width ; i++)
       {
         gotoxy(i,1);
         putchar(205);
```

(Contd.)

```
        gotoxy(i,hight);
        putchar(205);
      }


    for( i = 1 ; i <= hight ; i++)
      {
        gotoxy(1,i);
        putchar(186);
        gotoxy(width,i);
        putchar(186);
      }
        gotoxy(1,1);
        putchar(201);
        gotoxy(width,1);
        putchar(187);
        gotoxy(1,hight);
        putchar(200);
        gotoxy(width,hight);
        putchar(188);
        window(left+2, top+1, right-2, bottom-3);
        window(left, top, right, bottom+1);

    for( i = 0 ; i < 7 ; i++)
       {
          textcolor(i+2);
          gotoxy(i+3,i+2);
          cprintf("%s",string[i]);
       }

          gotoxy(10,hight-1);
          textcolor(RED | 128 );
          cputs("Press a key");
          getch();
          textcolor(WHITE);
}
```

Section IX

Program 1.

```
/* BREADTH FIRST SEARCH TECHNIQUE */
/* BFS.C */

# include<stdio.h>
# define size 20
# define T 1
# define F 0

struct Edge
{
   int terminal;
   struct Edge *next;
};

struct Vertex
{
   int visit;
   int vertex_no;
   char info;
   int path_length;
   struct Edge *Edge_Ptr;
};
struct Q
{
   int info;
   struct Q *next;
};
```

(Contd.)

```
void Table(int , int matrix [size][size], struct
Vertex vert[size]);
struct Edge *Insert_Vertex (int , struct Edge *);
void BFS ( int , struct Vertex vert [size]);
void Input(int, int mat [size][size]);
void Output(int number, int mat [size][size]);
struct Q *Insert_Queue(int vertex_no, struct Q
*first);
struct Q *Delete_Queue(int *vertex_no, struct Q
*first);

/* Insert vertex into connectivity list */

struct Edge * Insert_Vertex (int vertex_no, struct
Edge *first)    {
    struct Edge *new1, *current;
    new1 = (struct Edge *) malloc(sizeof(struct
    Edge));
    new1->terminal = vertex_no;
    new1->next = NULL;
    if (!first)
      return (new1);
    for (current = first; current->next; current =
    current->next);
    current->next = new1;
    return (first);
}

/* Insert vertices into queue */

struct Q * Insert_Queue(int vertex_no, struct Q
*first)
{
    struct Q *new1, *current;
    new1 =(struct Q *) malloc(sizeof(struct Q));
    new1->info = vertex_no;
    new1->next = NULL;
    if (!first)
      return (new1);
    for (current = first; current->next; current =
    current->next);
    current->next = new1;
```

(Contd.)

```
   return (first);
}

struct  Q * Delete_Queue(int *vertex_no, struct Q
*first)
{
   struct Q *previous;
   if (!first)
     return (NULL);
   *vertex_no = first->info;
   previous = first;
   first = first->next;
   free(previous);
   return (first);
}

/* Initializing entries */

void Table(int vertex_num, int matrix [size][size],
struct   Vertex vert[size])
{
    int i, j;
    for (i = 0; i < vertex_num; i++)
    {
     vert [i].visit = F;
     vert [i].vertex_no = i+1;
     vert [i].info = 'A'+ i;
     vert [i].path_length = 0;
     vert [i].Edge_Ptr = NULL;
    }

    for (i =0; i < vertex_num ; i++)
      for (j =0; j < vertex_num ; j++)
        if (matrix [i][j] > 0 )
          vert [i].Edge_Ptr = Insert_Vertex (j, vert
          [i].Edge_Ptr);
}

/* Computing path length */

void BFS ( int index, struct Vertex vert [size])
{
```

(Contd.)

```
    struct Q  *queue = NULL;
    struct Edge *Link;
    vert [index].visit = T;
    queue = Insert_Queue(index, queue);
    while(queue)
    {
      queue = Delete_Queue(&index, queue);
      for ( Link = vert [index].Edge_Ptr; Link; Link
      = Link->next)
      {
        if (vert [Link->terminal].visit == F)
        {
          vert[Link->terminal].visit = T;
          vert[Link->terminal].path_length =
          vert[index].path_length+1;
          queue = Insert_Queue(Link->terminal,
          queue);
        }
      }
    }
}

/* Input function to read adjacency matrix */

void Input(int number, int mat [size][size])
{
    int i, j;
    printf("\n Input the adjacency matrix \n");
    for (i =0; i < number; i++)
    {
      for (j=0; j < number; j ++)
      {
        scanf("%d", &mat [i][j]);
      }
      printf("\n");
    }
}

/* Output function to display adjacency matrix */

void Output(int number, int mat [size][size])
{
```

(Contd.)

```
    int i, j;
    printf("\n Adjacency matrix \n");
    for (i =0; i < number; i++)
    {
      for (j=0; j < number; j ++)
      {
        printf("   %d", mat [i][j]);
      }
      printf("\n");
    }
}

/* Function main */
void  main()
{
    int i, number, index;
    int mat [size][size];
    struct Vertex vert [size];
    struct Edge *List;
    printf("\n Input the number of vertices in the
    graph: ");
    scanf("%d", &number);
    Input(number, mat);
    Output(number, mat);
    Table(number, mat, vert);
    printf("\n Input the starting vertex 0- %d
    :",number-1);
    scanf("%d", &index);
    BFS (index, vert);
    printf("\n Path length of the vertex from %c",
    vert[index].info)
        ;
    printf("\n Vertex Length Vertex Connectivity
    \n ");
    for (i = 0; i < number; i++)
    {
      printf("\n   %c   %d   ",vert[i].info,
      vert[i].path_length);
      for (List= vert[i].Edge_Ptr; List; List =
      List->next)
      {
        printf(" ");
```

(Contd.)

```
        putchar(List->terminal+'A');
      }
    }
}
```

Program 2.

```
/* Create Binary TREE */
/* CREAT_BT.C */

# include<stdio.h>
# include<malloc.h>

struct NODE
{
    int Info;
    struct NODE *Left_Child;
    struct NODE *Right_Child;
};

struct NODE *Binary_Tree (char *, int, int);
void Output(struct NODE *, int );

/* Function to insert an element into tree */

struct  NODE *  Binary_Tree (char *List, int Lower,
int Upper)
{
    struct NODE *Node;
    int Mid = (Lower + Upper)/2;
    Node = (struct NODE *) malloc(sizeof(struct
    NODE));

    Node->Info = List [Mid];
    if ( Lower>= Upper)
    {
      Node->Left_Child = NULL;
      Node->Right_Child = NULL;
      return (Node);
    }

    if (Lower <= Mid - 1)
```

(Contd.)

```
    Node->Left_Child = Binary_Tree (List, Lower,
    Mid - 1);
   else
    Node->Left_Child = NULL;
   if (Mid + 1 <= Upper)
    Node->Right_Child = Binary_Tree (List, Mid +
    1, Upper);
   else
    Node->Right_Child = NULL;
   return(Node);
}

/* Output function */

void Output(struct NODE *T, int Level)
{
    int i;
    if (T)
    {
      Output(T->Right_Child, Level+1);
      printf("\n");
      for (i = 0; i < Level; i++)
        printf("   ");
      printf("%c", T->Info);
      Output(T->Left_Child, Level+1);
    }
}

/* Function main */

void main()
{
    char List[100];
    int Number = 0;
    char Info ;
    char choice;
    struct NODE *T = (struct NODE *)
    malloc(sizeof(struct NODE));
    T = NULL;
    printf("\n Input choice 'b' to break:");
    choice = getchar();
    while(choice != 'b')
```

(Contd.)

```
    {
      printf("\n Input information of the node: ");
      scanf("%c", &Info);
      List[Number++] = Info;
      fflush(stdin);
      printf("\n Input choice 'b' to break:");
      choice = getchar();
    }
    Number --;
    printf("\n Number of elements in the lsit is
    %d", Number);
    T = Binary_Tree(List, 0, Number);
    Output(T,1);
}
```

Program 3.

```
/* Create TREE */
/* CREAT_T.C */

# include<stdio.h>
# include<malloc.h>

struct NODE
{
    int Info;
    struct NODE *Left_Child;
    struct NODE *Right_Child;
};

struct NODE *Create_Tree (int , struct NODE *);
void Output(struct NODE *, int );

/* Function to create a tree */

struct NODE * Create_Tree (int Info, struct NODE
*Node)
{
    if (Node == NULL)
    {
      Node = (struct NODE *) malloc( sizeof(struct
      NODE ));
```

(Contd.)

```
      Node->Info = Info;
      Node->Left_Child = NULL;
      Node->Right_Child = NULL;
      return (Node);
    }

    /* Test for the left child */
    if (Node->Info >= Info )
      Node->Left_Child = Create_Tree (Info, Node-
      >Left_Child);
    else

         /* Set all the rest of the elements as
right child */

      Node->Right_Child = Create_Tree (Info, Node-
      >Right_Child);
    return(Node);
}

/* Output function */

void  Output(struct NODE *T, int Level)
{
    int i;
    if (T)
    {
      Output(T->Right_Child, Level+1);
      printf("\n ");
      for (i = 0; i < Level; i++)
        printf("   ");
      printf("%d", T->Info);
      printf("\n");
      Output(T->Left_Child, Level+1);
    }
}

/* Function main */

void main()
{
    int Info ;
```

(Contd.)

```
    char choice;
    struct NODE *T = (struct NODE *)
    malloc(sizeof(struct NODE *));
    T = NULL;
    printf("\n Input choice 'b' to break:");
    choice = getchar();
    while(choice != 'b')
    {
      printf("\n Input information of the node: ");
      scanf("%d", &Info);
      T = Create_Tree (Info, T);
      printf("\n Tree is ");
      Output(T, 1);
      printf("\n Input choice 'b' to break:");
      choice = getchar();
    }
}
```

Program 4.

```
/* DEPTH FIRST SEARCH TECHNIQUE */
/* DFS.C */

# include<stdio.h>
# define size 20
# define T 1
# define F 0

struct Edge
{
    int terminal;
    struct Edge *next;
};
struct Vertex
{
    int visit;
    int vertex_no;
    char info;
    int path_length;
    struct Edge *Edge_Ptr;
};
```

(Contd.)

```
void Table(int , int matrix [size][size], struct
Vertex vert[size]);
struct Edge *Insert_Vertex (int , struct Edge *);
void DFS ( int , int *dist, struct Vertex vert
[size]);
void Input(int, int a [size][size]);
void Output(int, int a [size][size]);

struct Edge * Insert_Vertex (int vertex_no, struct
Edge *first)
{
    struct Edge *new1, *current;
    new1 = (struct Edge *) malloc(sizeof(struct
    Edge));
    new1->terminal = vertex_no;
    new1->next = NULL;
    if (!first)
      return (new1);
    for (current = first; current->next; current =
    current->next);
    current->next = new1;
    return (first);
}

/* Initializing entries */
void Table(int vertex_num, int matrix [size][size],
struct Vertex vert[size])
{
    int i, j;
    for (i = 0; i < vertex_num; i++)
    {
      vert [i].visit = F;
      vert [i].vertex_no = i+1;
      vert [i].info = 'A'+ i;
      vert [i].path_length = 0;
      vert [i].Edge_Ptr = NULL;
    }

    for (i =0; i < vertex_num ; i++)
      for (j =0; j < vertex_num ; j++)
        if (matrix [i][j] > 0)
          vert [i].Edge_Ptr = Insert_Vertex (j, vert
```

(Contd.)

```
            [i].Edge_Ptr);
 }

 /* Computing path length */
 void DFS ( int index, int *dist,
 struct Vertex vert [size])
 {
     struct Edge *Link;
     vert [index].visit = T;
     vert [index].path_length = *dist;
     *dist += 1;
     for ( Link = vert [index].Edge_Ptr; Link; Link
     = Link->next)
       if (vert [Link->terminal].visit == F)
         DFS (Link->terminal, dist, vert);
 }

 /* Input function to read adjacency matrix */
 void Input(int number, int a [size][size])
 {
     int i, j;
     printf("\n Input the adjacency matrix \n");

     for (i =0; i < number; i++)
     {
       for (j=0; j < number; j ++)
       {
         scanf("%d", &a [i][j]);
       }
       printf("\n");
     }
 }

 /* Output function */
 void Output(int number, int a [size][size])
 {
     int i, j;
     printf("\n Adjacency matrix \n");
     for (i = 0; i < number; i++)
     {
       for (j = 0; j < number; j ++)
       {
```

(Contd.)

```
        printf("   %d", a [i][j]);
      }
      printf("\n");
    }
}

/* Function main */
void  main()
{
    int i;
    int number, index, dist;
    int a [size][size];
    struct Vertex vert [size];
    struct Edge *List;
    printf("\n Input the number of vertices in the
    graph: ");
    scanf("%d", &number);
    Input(number, a);
    Output(number, a);

    Table(number, a, vert);
    printf("\n Input the starting vertex 0- %d:",
    number-1);
    scanf("%d", &index);
    dist = 0;
    DFS (index, &dist, vert);
    printf("\n Path length of the vertex from %c",
    vert[index].info);
    printf("\n Vertex Length Vertex Connectivity
    \n ");
    for (i = 0; i < number; i++)
      {
      printf("\n  %c  %d   ", vert[i].info,
      vert[i].path_length);
      for (List= vert[i].Edge_Ptr; List; List
      = List->next)
      {
        printf(" ");
        putchar(List->terminal+'A');
      }
```

Program 5.

```
/* Double_i.c */
/* Inserting nodes in a double linked list */

#include <stdio.h>
#include <malloc.h>

void main(void)
{
    int i;

    struct ListEntry {
      int number;
      struct ListEntry *next;
      struct ListEntry *previous;
    } start, *node, *new;

    start.next = NULL;
    // Empty list
        start.previous = NULL;
    node = &start;
    // Point to the start of the list

        for (i = 1; i < 10; i += 2)
    {
      node->next = (struct ListEntry *)
      malloc(sizeof(struct ListEntry));
      node->next->previous = node;
      node = node->next;
      node->number = 50 + i;
      node->next = NULL;
    }

    /* Display the list */

    printf("\n List before inserting nodes\n ");

    node = start.next;
    do {
      printf("%d ", node->number);
      node = node->next;
```

(Contd.)

```
} while (node);

/* inserting some nodes in the list */

for (i = 2; i <= 10; i += 2)
{
  int found = 0;

  new = (struct ListEntry *)
  malloc(sizeof(struct ListEntry));
  new->number = 50 + i;
  node = start.next;

  do {
    if (node->number > new->number)
    {
      new->next = node;
      new->previous = node->previous;
      node->previous->next = new;
      node->previous = new;
      found = 1;
    }
    else
      node = node->next;
  } while ((node->next) && (! found));

  if (! found)
    if (node->number > new->number)
    {
      new->next = node;
      new->previous = node->previous;
      node->previous->next = new;
      node->previous = new;
    }
    else
    {
      new->next = NULL;
      new->previous = node;
      node->next = new;
    }
}
```

(Contd.)

```
    /* Display the list */

    printf("\n List after inserting nodes\n ");

    node = start.next;
    do {
      printf("%d ", node->number);
      node = node->next;
    } while (node);
}
```

Program 6.

```
/* Doubly linked list */
/* This program seg,ent creates a doubly linked
list then prints in forward and backword */

/* Double_l.c */

#include <stdio.h>
#include <malloc.h>

void main(void)
{
    int i;

    struct ListEntry {
      int number;
      struct ListEntry *next;
      struct ListEntry *previous;
    } start, *node;

    start.next = NULL;  /* Empty list */
    start.previous = NULL;
    node = &start;
              /* Point to the start of the list */

    for (i = 1; i <= 10; i++)
    {
      node->next = (struct ListEntry *)
      malloc(sizeof(struct ListEntry));
      node->next->previous = node;
```

(Contd.)

```
      node = node->next;
      node->number = 50+i;
      node->next = NULL;
    }

    /* Display the list */

    node = start.next;

    do {
      printf("%d ", node->number);
      node = node->next;
    } while (node->next);
                                  /* Show 60 only one time */

    do {
      printf("%d ", node->number);
      node = node->previous;
    } while (node->previous);
}
```

Program 7.

```
/* Filelist.c */

#include <stdio.h>
#include <dirent.h>
#include <malloc.h>
#include <string.h>
#include <stdlib.h>

void main(int argc, char *argv[])
{
    DIR *directory_pointer;
    struct dirent *entry;

    struct FileList {
      char filename[64];
      struct FileList *next;
    } start, *node;

    if ((directory_pointer = opendir(argv[1])) ==
    NULL)printf("Error opening %s\n", argv[1]);
```

(Contd.)

```
    else
    {
      start.next = NULL;
      node = &start;

      while (entry = readdir(directory_pointer))
      {
        node->next = (struct FileList *)
        malloc(sizeof(struct FileList));
        if (node == NULL)
        {
          printf(" Insufficient memory to store
          list \n");
          exit(1);
        }
        node = node->next;
    strcpy(node->filename, entry->d_name);
        node->next = NULL;
      }

      closedir(directory_pointer);


      node = &start;

      while (node)
      {
        printf("%s\n", node->filename);
        node = node->next;
      }

    }
}
```

Program 8.

```
/* LINK.C */
/* This program segment defines linked list having
a character type node */

# include<stdio.h>
# include<malloc.h>
```

(Contd.)

```
   struct list
         {
          char data ;
          struct list *next ;
     } ;

typedef  struct list Linked;

void main()
 {
  Linked *start, node1, node2 , node3 , node4;
      int i ;
   start = (struct list *)
   malloc(sizeof(Linked));
     start = &node1;

     node1.data = 'A' ;
     node1.next = &node2;

     node2.data = 'B' ;
     node2.next = &node3;

     node3.data = 'C' ;
     node3.next = &node4;
     node4.data = 'D' ;

for( i = 0 ; i < 4 ; i++ )
{
  printf("\n %c", start->data);
  start = start->next ;
  printf("\nPress a key");
  getchar();
 }
 }
```

Program 9.

```
/* CREATING SIMPLE LINKED LIST */
/* LINK_C.C */

# include <stdio.h>
# include <malloc.h>
```

(Contd.)

```
struct link
{
    int info;
    struct link *next;
};

int i;
struct link *start = NULL; /* Shows empty list */

void creat_link_list (struct link *);
void display (struct link *);

void creat_link_list (struct link *node)
{
    char ch;
    printf("\n Input choice n for break: ");
    i = 0;
    ch = getchar();
    while(ch !='n')
    {
      printf("\n Input the node: %d :", i+1);
      scanf("%d",&node->info);
      node->next = (struct link* ) malloc (sizeof
      (struct link));
      node = node->next;
      node->next = start;
      i++;
      printf("\n Input choice n for break: ");
      ch = getchar();
    }
}

/* Display the list */

void  display(struct link *node)
{
    printf("\n Values of the entered nodes are as
    follows:\n");
    while (node)
    {
      printf("  %d", node->info);
      node = node->next;
```

(Contd.)

```
    }
}

/* Function main */

void main()
{
    struct link *node = (struct link *)
    malloc(sizeof(struct link));
    creat_link_list(node);
    display(node);
}
```

Program 10.

```
/* LINK_N.C */
/* This program segment define linked list having
string type node */

# include<stdio.h>
# include<malloc.h>

struct list
{
    char data[30];
    struct list *next ;
};
typedef  struct list linked;

void main()
{
    linked *start, node1, node2 , node3 , node4;
    int i ;

    start = (struct list *) malloc(sizeof(linked));
    start = &node1;

    gets(node1.data);

    node1.next = &node2;

    gets(node2.data) ;
```

(Contd.)

```
    node2.next = &node3;

    gets(node3.data) ;
    node3.next = &node4;
    gets(node4.data);

    node4.next = '\0' ;
    printf("\n Output is\n");
    do
    {
      printf("\n %s",start->data);
      printf("\n Press a key");
      getchar() ;
      start = start->next ;
    } while(start->next!='\0');
}
```

Program 11.

```
/* PEEP OPERATION ON THE STACK USING ARRAYS */
/* PEEPCH.C */

# include<stdio.h>
# include<string.h>
# include<ctype.h>

# define size  100

int top = -1;
int flag = 0;

int stack[100];
int data;

void push(int *, int);
int peep(int *);
void display(int *);

/* Definition of the push function */

void  push(int s[], int d)
{
```

(Contd.)

```
    if(top ==(size-1))
      flag = 0;
    else
    {
      flag = 1;
      ++top;
      s[top] = d;

    }
}

/* Definition of the peep function */

int peep(int s[])
{
    int i;
    int peeped_element;
    printf("\n Input the information number to
    which you want access:");
    scanf("%d", &i);

    if(top - i + 1 < 0)
    {
      peeped_element = 0;
      flag = 0;
    }
    else
    {
      flag = 1;
      peeped_element = s[top-i +1];
    }
    return (peeped_element);
}

/* Definition of the display function */
void display(int s[])
{
    int i;
    if(top == -1)
    {
      printf("Stack is empty");
    }
```

(Contd.)

```
    else
    {
      for(i = top; i>=0; --i)
        printf(" %d  ", s[i]);
    }
}

/* Function main */

void main()
{
    int  data;
    char choice;
    int q = 0;
    int top = -1;

    do
    {
      printf(" \nPush->i Peep->p Quit->q:");
      printf("\nInput the choice : ");
      do
      {
        choice = getchar();
        choice =tolower(choice);
      }while(strchr("ipq",choice)==NULL);
      printf("Your choice is: ", choice);

      switch(choice)
      {
      case 'i' :
        printf("\n Input the element to push:");
        scanf("%d", &data);
        push(stack, data);
        if(flag)
        {
          printf("\n After inserting ");
          display(stack);
          if(top == (size-1))
            printf("\n Stack is full");
        }
        else
          printf("\n Stack overflow after pushing");
```

(Contd.)

```
      break;

    case 'p' :
      data = peep(stack);
      if(flag)
      {
        printf("\n Data is peeped: %d", data);
        printf("\n Stack is as follows:\n");

        display(stack);
      }
      else
        printf("\n Stack underflow");
      break;
    case 'q':
      q = 1;
    }
  } while(!q);
}
```

Program 12.

```
/* postfix.c */

# include<stdio.h>
# include<string.h>
# include<ctype.h>
# include<stdlib.h>

# define Arnold '\0'
# define Blank ' '
# define Tab '\t'

#define Maxlen 64

static char infix [Maxlen+1], stack[Maxlen],
postfix[Maxlen+1];

# define Empty (-1) /* empty stack */
static int top;

/* symbol types */
```

(Contd.)

```
#define Operator (-10)
# define Operand (-20)

# define LeftParen (-30)
# define RightParen (-40)

static char *symbols = "()+-%*/";

/* Symbol precedence */

# define LeftParenPrec 0  /* ( */
# define AddPrec 1 /* + */
# define SubPrec 1 /* - */
# define MultPrec 2 /* * */
# define DivPrec 2 /* / */
# define RemPrec 2 /* % */
# define None 999 /* all else */

void read_input(void);
void infix_to_postfix(void);
void write_output(void);
void push(char symbol);
char pop (void);

int get_type(char );
int get_prec(char );
int white_space(char );

void full_stack();
void empty_stack();

void main()
{
    char ans[2];
    do
    {
      top = Empty; /* reset stack */
      read_input();
      infix_to_postfix();
      write_output();

      /* Selection */
```

(Contd.)

```
    printf("\n\n Another (y/n)");
    gets(ans);
  } while (toupper(ans[0]) == 'Y');
}

/* function infix to postfix conversion */
void infix_to_postfix(void)
{
  int i,p, len, type, precedence;
  char next ;

  /* i for infix, p for postfix */

  i = p = 0;
  len = strlen(infix);

  /* loop through input string */
  while(i < len)
  {
    /* ignore whitepsce in infix expression */
    if( !white_space(infix[i]))
    {
      type = get_type(infix[i]);
      switch(type)
      {
        /* push left paren onto stack */
      case LeftParen:
        push(infix[i]);
        break;

        /* pop stack until matching left paren */
      case RightParen:
        while((next = pop()) != '(')
          postfix[p++] = next;
        break;
      case Operand: postfix[p++] = infix[i];
        break;
        /* Pop stack until first operator of
higher precedence and then stack this operator */

      case Operator:
        precedence = get_prec(infix[i]);
```

(Contd.)

```
          /* Anything on stack to pop */
          while(top > Empty && precedence<=
          get_prec(stack[top]))
            postfix[p++] = pop();
          push(infix[i]);
          break;
        }
      }
      i++; /* next symbol in infix expression */
    }

    /* pop any remaining operators */
    while(top > Empty ) postfix[p++] = pop();
    postfix[p] = Arnold ; /* ensure a string */
}

/* Function to find operator type */

int get_type(char symbol )
{
    switch(symbol)
    {
    case '(' :
      return (LeftParen);
    case ')':
      return (RightParen);
    case '+':
    case '-':
    case '%':
    case '*':
    case '/':
      return (Operator);
    default:
      return (Operand);
    }
}

/* Find precedence of the operator */

int get_prec(char symbol )
{
    switch(symbol)
    {
```

(Contd.)

```
    case '+':
      return (AddPrec);
    case '-':
      return (SubPrec);
    case '*':
      return (MultPrec);
    case '/':
      return (DivPrec);
    case '%':
      return (RemPrec);
    case '(':
      return (LeftParenPrec);
    default:
      return (None);
    }
}

/* Function push */

void push(char symbol)
{
    /* check for overflow */
    if(top > Maxlen)
      full_stack();
    else
      stack[++top] = symbol;
}

/* Function pop */

char pop(void)
{
    /* check for underflow */
    if (top <= Empty )
      empty_stack();
    else
      return (stack[top--]);
}

/* Exit in case of overflow */

void full_stack(void )
{
```

(Contd.)

```
        printf("\n Full Stsck ... exiting. \n");
        exit(1);
    }

    /* Exit in case of underflow */
    void empty_stack(void)
    {
        printf("\n Empty Stack ... exiting \n");
        exit(2);
    }

    void read_input(void)
    {
        printf("\n Infix (up to %d chars): ", Maxlen);
        gets(infix);
    }


    /* Output function */
    void write_output(void)
    {
        printf("\n Infix: %s", infix);
        printf("\n Postfix: %s \n",postfix);
    }

    /* function white space checking */

    int white_space(char symbol)
    {
        return( symbol == Blank || symbol == Tab ||
    symbol == Arnold);
    }
```

Program 13.

```
    /* INSERTION AND DELETION IN A QUEUE ARRAY
    IMPLEMENTATION */

    # include<stdio.h>
    # include<string.h>
    # include<ctype.h>
    # include<stdlib.h>
```

(Contd.)

```
# define size 10

int rear, front;
int ch;
int q[size];

int rear = 0;
int front = 0;
void Insert_queue();
void Delete_queue();
void Display_queue();

/* Function to create queue */

void  Insert_queue()
{
    printf("\n Input the element :");
    scanf("%d", &ch);
    if(rear < size)
    {
      rear ++;
      q[rear] = ch ;
      if(front == 0)
        front = 1;
    }
    else
      printf("\n Queue is overflow");
}

/* Function to perform delete operation */

void Delete_queue()
{
    if (front == 0)
    {
      printf("\n Underflow");
      return ;
    }
    else
    {
      ch = q[front];
```

(Contd.)

```
      printf("\n Element deleted : %d", ch);
    }
    if(front == rear)
    {
      front = 0;
      rear = 0;
    }
    else
      front = front + 1;
}

/* Output function */

void Display_queue()  //char q[])
{
    int i;
    if (front == 0)
      return;
    for(i = front ; i <= rear; i++)
      printf(" %d ", q[i]);
}

/* Function main */

void main()
{
    int k = 0;
    char choice;

    do
    {
      printf("\nInsert->i Delete->d Quit->q:");
      printf("\nInput the choice : ");
      do
      {
        choice = getchar();
        choice = tolower(choice);
      }while(strchr("idq",choice)==NULL);
      printf("Your choice is: %c ", choice);

      switch(choice)
```

(Contd.)

```
        {
        case 'i' :
          Insert_queue();
          printf("\nQueue after inserting ");
          Display_queue();
          break;

        case 'd' :
          Delete_queue();
          printf("\nQueue content after deleteion is
          as follows:\n");
          Display_queue();
          break;

        case 'q':
          k = 1;
        }
      } while(!k);
}
```

Program 14.

```
/* INSERTION AND DELETION IN A CIRCULAR QUEUE ARRAY
IMPLEMENTATION */
/* QUEUEID.C */

# include<stdio.h>
# include<string.h>
# include<ctype.h>
# include<stdlib.h>

# define size 6

int L, U;
     /* L means lower bound U means upper bound */

int rear, front;
int ch;
int q[size];

int rear = -1;
```

(Contd.)

```
int front = -1;
void Insert_queue();
void Delete_queue();
void Display_queue();

/* Function to create queue */

void Insert_queue()
{
    if ((front == 0) && (rear == size-1))
    {
      printf("\n Overflow");
      rear = 1;
      return;
    }
    else
      if (front < 0) /* Insert first element */
      {
        front = 0;
        rear = 0;
        printf("\nInput the element :");
        scanf("%d", &ch);
        q[rear] = ch ;
      }
      else
        if (rear == size-1)
        {
          rear = 0;
          printf("\n Input the element :");
          scanf("%d", &ch);
          q[rear] = ch ;
        }

        else
        {
          rear ++;
          printf("\n Input the element :");
          scanf("%d", &ch);
          q[rear] = ch ;
        }
}
```

(Contd.)

```
/* Function to perform delete operation */
void Delete_queue()
{
    if (front < 0)
    {
      printf("\nUnderflow");
      return ;
    }
    ch = q[front];
    q[front] = NULL;
    printf("\n Element deleted :", ch);
    if(front == rear)
    {
      front = -1;
      rear = -1;
    }
    else
      if ( front == size-1)
      {
        front = 0;
      }
      else
      {
        front++ ;
      }

}

/* Output function */

void Display_queue()
{
    int i;
    if (front < 0)
      return;
    if ( rear >= front)
    {
      for(i = front; i <= rear; i++)
      {
        printf("\n i = %d", i);
        printf(" %d ", q[i]);
      }
```

(Contd.)

```
    }
    else
    {
      for(i = front; i < size; i++)
      {
        printf("\n i = %d", i);
        printf(" %d", q[i]);
      }
      for(i = 0; i <= rear; i++)
      {
        printf("\n i = %d", i);
        printf(" %d ", q[i]);
      }
    }
}

/* Function main  */

void main()
{
    int k = 0;
    char choice;

    do
    {
      printf("\nInsert->i Delete->d Quit->q:");
      printf("\nInput the choice : ");
      do
      {
        choice = getchar();
        choice = tolower(choice);
      }while(strchr("idq",choice)==NULL);
      printf("Your choice is: %c",choice);

      switch(choice)
      {
      case 'i' :
        Insert_queue();
        printf("\nQueue after inserting ");
        Display_queue();
        break;

      case 'd' :
```

(Contd.)

```
      Delete_queue();
      printf("\nQueue content after deleteion is
      as follows:\n");
      Display_queue();
      break;

    case 'q':
      k = 1;
    }
  } while(!k);
}
```

Program 15.

```
/* removes.c */

#include <stdio.h>
#include <malloc.h>

void main(void)
{
    int i;

    struct ListEntry {
      int number;
      struct ListEntry *next;
    } start, *node, *previous;

    start.next = NULL;  /* Empty list */
    node = &start;
/* Point to the start of the list */

    for (i = 1; i <= 10; i++)
    {
      node->next = (struct ListEntry *)
      malloc(sizeof(struct ListEntry));
      node = node->next;
      node->number = 50+i;
      node->next = NULL;
    }

    /*  Remove the number 55 */
```

(Contd.)

```
    node = start.next;
    printf("\n List before deletion\n");
    while (node)
    {
      printf("%d ", node->number);
      node = node->next;
    }

    node = start.next;
    previous = &start;
    while (node)
      if (node->number == 55)
      {
        previous->next = node->next;
        free(node);
        break;         /* End the loop */
      }
      else
      {
        node = node->next;
        previous = previous->next;
      }

    /* Display the list */
    node = start.next;
    printf("\n List after deletion \n");
    while (node)
    {
      printf("%d ", node->number);
      node = node->next;
    }
}
```

Program 16.

```
/* removes_.c */
/* This program segment removes a node from a
doubly linked list */

#include <stdio.h>
#include <malloc.h>
```

(Contd.)

```
void main(void)
{
    int i, found;

    struct ListEntry {
      int number;
      struct ListEntry *next;
      struct ListEntry *previous;
    } start, *node;

    start.next = NULL;
    /* Empty list */
        start.previous = NULL;
    node = &start;
    /* Point to the start of the list */

        for (i = 1; i <= 10; i++)
    {
      node->next = (struct ListEntry *)
      malloc(sizeof(struct ListEntry));
      node->next->previous = node;
      node = node->next;
      node->number = 50 + i;
      node->next = NULL;
    }

    /* Display the list */

    printf("\n List before deletion \n");
    node = start.next;
    do {
      printf("%d ", node->number);
      node = node->next;
    } while (node);

    /* Remove the entry */

    node = start.next;
    found = 0;

    do {
      if (node->number == 57)
```

(Contd.)

```
        {
          found = 1;
          node->previous->next = node->next;
          node->next->previous = node->previous;
          free(node);
        }
        else
          node = node->next;
      } while ((node) && (! found));

      /* Display the list */

      printf("\n List after deletion \n");
      node = start.next;

      do {
        printf("%d ", node->number);
        node = node->next;
      } while (node);
}
```

Program 17.

```
/* sortlist.c */

#include <stdio.h>
#include <dirent.h>
#include <malloc.h>
#include <string.h>
#include <stdlib.h>

void main(int argc, char *argv[])
{
    DIR *directory_pointer;
    struct dirent *entry;

    struct FileList {
      char filename[64];
      struct FileList *next;
    } start, *node, *previous, *new;

    if ((directory_pointer = opendir(argv[1])) ==
```

(Contd.)

```
NULL)printf("Error opening %s\n", argv[1]);
else
{
  start.next = NULL;

  while (entry = readdir(directory_pointer))
  {
    /* Find the correct location */
        previous = &start;
    node = start.next;
    while ((node) && (strcmp(entry->d_name,
    node->filename) > 0))
    {
      node = node->next;
      previous = previous->next;
    }

    new = (struct FileList *)
    malloc(sizeof(struct FileList));
    if (new == NULL)
    {
      printf("Insufficient memory to store
      list \n");
      exit(1);
    }
    new->next = node;
    previous->next = new;
    strcpy(new->filename, entry->d_name);
  }

  closedir(directory_pointer);


  node = start.next;

  while (node)
  {
    printf("%s\n", node->filename);
    node = node->next;
  }
 }
}
```

Program 18.

```
/* IMPLEMENTATION OF THE STACK USING ARRAYS */
/* STACK_A.C */

# include<stdio.h>
# include<string.h>
# include<ctype.h>

# define size  100


int top = -1;
int flag = 0;
int stack[size];

void push(int *, int);
int pop(int *);
void display(int *);

/* Definition of the push function */

void push(int s[], int d)
{
    if(top ==(size-1))
      flag = 0;
    else
    {
      flag = 1;
      s[top] = d;
      ++top;
    }
}

/* Definition of the pop function */

int pop(int s[])
{
    int popped_element;
    if(top == -1)
    {
      popped_element = 0;
```

(Contd.)

```
        flag = 0;
      }
      else
      {
        flag = 1;
        popped_element = s[top];
        --top;
      }
      return (popped_element);
}

/* Definition of the display function */

void display(int s[])
{
      int i;
      if(top == -1)
      {
        printf("\n Stack is empty");
      }
      else
      {
        for(i = top; i >= 0; --i)
          printf("\n %d", s[i] );
      }
}

/* Function main */

void main()
{

      int  data;
      char choice;
      int q = 0;
      int top = -1;

      do
      {
        printf(" \nPush->i Pop->p Quit->q:");
        printf("\nInput the choice : ");
        do
        {
```

(Contd.)

```
    choice = getchar();
    choice =tolower(choice);
  }while(strchr("ipq",choice)==NULL);
  printf("Your choice is: %c",choice);

  switch(choice)
  {
  case 'i' :
    printf("\n Input the element to push:");
    scanf("%d", &data);
    push(stack, data);
    if(flag)
    {
      printf("\n After inserting ");
      display(stack);
      if(top == (size-1))
        printf("\n Stack is full");
    }
    else
      printf("\n Stack overflow after pushing");
    break;

  case 'p' :
    data = pop(stack);
    if(flag)
    {
      printf("\n Data is popped: %d", data);
      printf("\n Rest data in stack is as
      follows:\n");

      display(stack);
    }
    else
      printf("\n Stack underflow" );
    break;
  case 'q':
    q = 1;
  }
} while(!q);
```

Program 19.

```
/* STACK IMPLEMENTATION USING LINKED LIST */
/* STACK_L.C */

# include<stdio.h>
# include<malloc.h>

struct link
{
    int info;
    struct link *next;
} *start;


void display(struct link *);
struct link *push(struct link *);
struct link *pop(struct link *);
int main_menu();

void display(struct link *rec)
{
    while(rec != NULL)
    {
      printf(" %d ",rec->info);
      rec = rec->next;
    }
}

struct link * push(struct link *rec)
{
    struct link *new_rec;
    printf("\n Input the new value for next
    location of the stack:");

    new_rec = (struct link *)malloc(sizeof(struct
    link));
    scanf("%d", &new_rec->info);
    new_rec->next = rec;
    rec = new_rec;
    return(rec);
}
```

(Contd.)

```
struct  link * pop(struct link *rec)
{
    struct link *temp;

    if(rec == NULL)
    {
      printf("\n Stack is empty");
    }
    else
    {
      temp = rec->next;
      free(rec);
      rec = temp;
      printf("\n After pop operation the stack is as
      follows:\n");
      display(rec);
      if(rec  == NULL)
        printf("\n Stack is empty");
    }
    return(rec);
}

int main_menu ()
{
    int choice;
    do
    {
      printf("\n 1<-Push ");
      printf("\n 2<-Pop");
      printf("\n 3<-Quit");
      printf("\n Input your choice :");
      scanf("%d", &choice);
      if(choice <1 || choice >3)
        printf("\n Incorrect choice-> Try once
        again");
    } while(choice <1 || choice >3);

    return(choice);
}

/* main function */
```

(Contd.)

```
void main()
{
    struct link *start ;
    int choice;
    start = NULL;
    do
    {
      choice = main_menu();
      switch(choice)
      {
      case 1:
        start = push(start);
        printf("\n After push operation stack is as
        follows:\n");
        display(start);
        break;
      case 2:
        start = pop(start);
        break;
      default :
        printf("\n End of session");
      }
    } while(choice != 3);
}
```

Program 20.

```
#include <stdio.h>
#include <alloc.h>

void main(void)
 {
   int i;

   struct ListEntry {
     int number;
     struct ListEntry *next;
   } start, *node;

   start.next = NULL;  // Empty list

   node = &start;      // Point to the start of the
    list
```

(Contd.)

```
    for (i = 1; i <= 10; i++)
      {
       node->next = (struct ListEntry *)
       malloc(sizeof(struct ListEntry));
       node = node->next;
       node->number = i;
       node->next = NULL;
      }

    // Display the list

    node = start.next;

    while (node)
      {
       printf("%d ", node->number);
       node = node->next;
      }
}
```

Section X

Program 1.

```
/* binary.c */

#include <stdio.h>

int binary_search(int array[], int value, int size)
{
    int found = 0;
    int high = size, low = 0, mid;

    mid = (high + low) / 2;

    printf("\n\nLooking for %d\n", value);

    while ((! found) && (high >= low))
    {
      printf("Low %d Mid %d High %d\n", low, mid,
      high);

      if (value == array[mid])
        found = 1;
      else if (value < array[mid])
        high = mid - 1;
      else
        low = mid + 1;

      mid = (high + low) / 2;
    }
    return((found) ? mid: -1);
}
```

(Contd.)

```
void main(void)
{
    int array[100], i;

    for (i = 0; i < 100; i++)
      array[i] = i+20;

    printf("Result of search %d\n",
    binary_search(array, 33, 100));
    printf("Result of search %d\n",
    binary_search(array, 75, 100));
    printf("Result of search %d\n",
    binary_search(array, 1, 100));
}
```

Program 2.

```
/* BUBBLE SORT FOR SORTING STRINGS */
/* BUB_STR.C */

# include <stdlib.h>
# include <string.h>
# include <malloc.h>
# include <stdio.h>

void bubble_sort(char *array[], int );
void display(char *list[], int);

void bubble_sort(char *array[], int size)
{
    char *temp;
    int i, j;
    for (i = 0; i < size; i++)
      for (j = 0; j < size-i-1; j++)
        if (strcmp(array[j], array[j+1]) < 0)
        {
          temp =(char *) malloc(sizeof(array[j]));
          temp = array[j];
          array[j] = array[j+1];
          array[j+1] = temp;
        }
}
```

(Contd.)

```
void display(char *list[], int n)
{
    int i;
    for(i = 0 ; i < n; i++)
    {
      printf("\n %s", list[i]);
    }
}

void main(void)
{
    char *list[100] = {
                        "MONDAY",
                        "TUESDAY",
                        "WEDNESDAY",
                        "FRIDAY",
                        "SATURDAY"
                         };
    printf("\n Input list is as follows:");
    display(list, 5);
    bubble_sort(list, 5);
    printf("\n Sorted list is as follows:\n");
    display(list, 5);
}
```

Program 3.

```
/* bubble.c */

#include <stdio.h>
#include <stdlib.h>

void bubble_sort(int array[], int size)
{
    int temp, i, j;

    for (i = 0; i < size; i++)
      for (j = 0; j < size-i-1; j++)
        if (array[j] < array[j+1])
        {
          temp = array[j];
          array[j] = array[j+1];
```

(Contd.)

```
            array[j+1] = temp;
          }
    }

    void main(void)
    {
        int values[30], i;
        printf("\n Unsorted list is as follows\n");

        for (i = 0; i < 10; i++)
        {
                values[i] = rand() % 100;
          printf(" %d", values[i]);
        }
        bubble_sort(values, 10);
        printf("\n Sorted list is as follows\n");

        for (i = 0; i < 10; i++)
          printf("%d ", values[i]);
    }
```

Program 4.

```
    /* HEAP SORT */
    /* HEAP.C */

    # include<stdio.h>

    void  heap_sort(int *, int );
    void create_heap(int *, int);
    void display(int *, int);

    /*  Definition of the function */

    void create_heap(int list[], int n )
    {

        int k, j, i, temp;

        for(k = 2 ; k <= n;  ++k)
        {
          i = k ;
```

(Contd.)

```
    temp = list[k];
    j = i / 2 ;

    while((i > 1) && (temp > list[j]))
    {
      list[i] = list[j];
      i = j ;
      j = i / 2 ;
      if ( j < 1 )
        j = 1 ;
    }

    list[i] = temp ;
  }
}

/* End of heap creation function */

/* Definition of the function */

void heap_sort(int list[], int n)
{
    int k, temp, value, j, i, p;
    int step = 1;
    for(k = n ; k >= 2; --k)
    {
      temp = list[1] ;
      list[1] = list[k];
      list[k] = temp ;

      i = 1 ;
      value = list[1];
      j = 2 ;

      if((j+1) < k)
        if(list[j+1] > list[j])
          j ++;
      while((j <= ( k-1)) && (list[j] > value))
      {
        list[i] = list[j];
        i = j ;
        j = 2*i ;
```

(Contd.)

```
        if((j+1) < k)
          if(list[j+1] > list[j])
            j++;
          else
            if( j > n)
              j = n ;
        list[i] = value;
      } /* end of while statement */

      printf("\n Step = %d ", step);
      step++;
      for(p = 1; p <= n; p++)
        printf(" %d", list[p]);
    } /* end for loop */
}

/* Display function */

void display(int list[], int n)
{
    int i;
    for(i = 1 ; i <= n; ++ i)
    {
      printf("  %d", list[i]);
    }
}

/* Function main */

void main()
{
    int list[100];
    int i, size = 13 ;

    printf("\n Size of the list: %d", size);

    for(i = 1 ; i <= size ; ++i)
    {
      list[i] = rand() % 100;
    }
    printf("\n Entered list is as follows:\n");
    display(list, size);
```

(Contd.)

```
    create_heap(list, size);
    printf("\n Heap\n");
    display(list, size);
    printf("\n\n");

    heap_sort(list,size);

    printf("\n\n Sorted list is as follows :\n\n");
    display(list,size);

}
```

Program 5.

```
/* INSERTION SORT */
/* INSERS.C */

# include<stdio.h>
# include<stdlib.h>

int key;

int  insertion_sort(int *);
// prototype
void display(int *, int);

/* Definition of the insertion sort function */

int insertion_sort(int list[])
{
    int i = 0;
    int j, k ;
    printf("\nElement to be inserted Break
    condition is -0 : ");
    scanf("%d", &key);
    printf("\n Selected Element is: %d", key);

    while(key != -0 ) /* -0 is break condition */
    {
      k = i - 1;
      while((key < list[k]) && (k >= 0))
      {
```

(Contd.)

```
        list[k+1] = list[k];
        --k;
      }

      list[k+1] = key ;
      printf("\n List after inserting an element ");
      for(j = 0 ; j<=i; j++)
        printf(" %d", list[j]);

      printf("\n Element to be inserted Break
      condition is -0: ");
      scanf("%d", &key);
      printf("\n Selected Element is: %d", key);
      i ++;

    }
    return i;
}

/* End of the insertion sort function */

/* Definition of the function */

void display(int list[], int n)
{
    int j;
    printf("\n Final sorted list is as
    follows:\n");
    for(j = 0 ; j < n ; j++)
      printf(" %d", list[j]);
}

/* End of the display function */

void main()
{
    int list[200];
    int n ;

    n = insertion_sort(list);
    display(list,n);
}
```

Program 6.

```
/* Insertion sort */
/* INSERT.C */

# include<stdio.h>
# include<stdlib.h>

void insertion_sort(int *, int);
void display(int*, int);

void insertion_sort(int l[], int n)
{
    int pointer, temp;
    int i, k;

    l[0] = -0;
    for(i = 1 ; i <= n; i++)
    {
      pointer = i -1;
      temp = l[i];
      while(temp < l[pointer])
      {
        l[pointer+1] = l[pointer];
        pointer --;
      }
      l[pointer+1] = temp;
      printf("Step = %d", i);
      for(k = 0; k <= n; k++)
        printf(" %d", l[k]);
      printf("\n");
    }
}

void display(int l[], int n)
{
int i;
    printf("\n Sorted list is as follows\n");
    for(i = 1; i <= n; i++)
      printf(" %d", l[i]);
}
```

(Contd.)

```
void main()
{
    int number = 10;
    int list[100];
    int i;

    printf("\n Number of elements in the list: %i",
    number);
    printf("\n Unsorted list is as follows \n");

    for(i = 1; i <= number; i++)
    {
      list[i] = rand() %100;
      printf(" %d", list[i]);
    }
    printf("\n");

    printf("\n Step wise result is as follows
    \n\n");

    insertion_sort(list,number);
    display(list, number);
}
```

Program 7.

```
/* LINEAR SEARCH */
/* lsearch.c */

# include<stdio.h>


int search;
int flag;
int    input( int *, int , int);

void linear_search(int * , int , int );
void display(int *, int);

/* Definition of function */

void  linear_search(int l[], int n, int element)
{
```

(Contd.)

```
    int k;
    flag = 1;
    for(k = 0; k< n; k++)
    {
      if(l[k] == element)
      {
        printf("\n Search is successful \n");
        printf("\n Element: %i Found at Location:
        %i", element,
             k+1);
        flag = 0 ;
      }
    }
    if (flag)
      printf("\n Search is unsuccessful");
}

void display(int list[], int n)
{
    int i;
    for(i = 0 ; i < n ; i++)
    {
      printf(" %d", list[i]);
    }
}
input(int list[], int number, int key)
{
    int i;
    key = 30;
    printf("Input the number of elements in the
    list:");
    number = 20;
    for(i = 0 ; i < 20; i++)
    {
      list[i] = rand() %100;
    }
    printf("\n Element to be searched: %d", key);
    search = key;
    return number;
}
void main()
{
```

(Contd.)

```
    int number, key, list[200];

    number = input( list, number, key);

    key = search ;
    printf("\n Entered list as follows:\n");
    display(list,number);
    linear_search(list, number, key);
    printf("\n In the following list\n");
    display(list,number);
}
```

Program 8.

```
/* MERGE SORT */
/* merge.c */

# include<stdio.h>
# include<stdlib.h>

void merge_sort(float *, int , int , int );
void merge_pass(float *, int , int );

/* Definitior of the function */

void merge_sort(float l[], int top, int size, int
bottom)
{
    float temp[1000];
    int f = top;
    int s = size +1 ;
    int t = top ;
    int upper;
    while(( f <= size)&&(s <=bottom))
    {
      if(l[f] <= l[s])
      {
        temp[t] = l[f] ;
        f ++;
      }

      else
      {
```

(Contd.)

```
      temp[t] = l[s] ;
      s ++;
    }

    t ++;
  }

  if(f <=size)
  {
    for(f = f ; f<=size; f++)
    {
      temp[t] = l[f];
      t++;
    }
  }

  else
  {
    for(s = s ; s<= bottom ; s++)
    {
      temp[t]=l[s];
      t++;
    }

  }

  for(upper = top; upper <= bottom ; upper++)
  {
    l[upper]=temp[upper];
  }

}

/* Definition of the function */

void merge_pass( float append[], int m, int n )
{
  if( m!= n)
  {
    int mid = (m+n)/2;
    merge_pass( append, m, mid );
```

(Contd.)

```
        merge_pass( append, mid+1, n );
        merge_sort( append, m, mid, n );
      }
}

/* main function */

void main()
{
    float list[1000];
    int i, n = 30;
    printf("\n Size of the list: %d", n);

    for(i = 0 ; i < n ; i++)
    {
      list[i] = (float) (rand() %100);
    }

    printf("\n Entered list as follows:\n");
    for( i = 0 ; i<n ; i++)
      printf(" %d ", (int) list[i]);

    i = 0 ;

    merge_pass(list, i, n-1);

    printf("\n Merge sorted list is as
follows:\n");
    for( i = 0 ; i<n ; i++)
      printf(" %d", (int) list[i]);
}
```

Program 9.

```
/* quick.c */

#include <stdio.h>
#include <stdlib.h>

void quick_sort(int array[], int first, int last)
{
    int temp, low, high, pivot;
```

(Contd.)

```
    low = first;
    high = last;
    pivot = array[(first + last) / 2];

    do {
      while (array[low] < pivot)
        low++;

      while (array[high] > pivot)
        high--;

      if (low <= high)
      {
        temp = array[low];
        array[low++] = array[high];
        array[high--] = temp;
      }
    } while (low <= high);

    if (first < high)
      quick_sort(array, first, high);
    if (low < last)
      quick_sort(array, low, last);
}

void main(void)
{
    int values[100], i;
    printf("\n Unsorted list is as follows \n");

    for (i = 0; i < 20; i++)
    {
      values[i] = rand() % 100;
      printf(" %d", values[i]);
    }
    quick_sort(values, 0, 19);

    printf("\n Sorted list as follows\n");

    for (i = 0; i < 20; i++)
      printf("%d ", values[i]);
}
```

Program 10.

```
/* select.c */
/* selection sort */

#include <stdio.h>
#include <stdlib.h>

void selection_sort(int array[], int size)
{
    int temp, current, j;

    for (current = 0; current < size; current++)
      for (j = current + 1; j < size; j++)
        if (array[current] > array[j])
        {
          temp = array[current];
          array[current] = array[j];
          array[j] = temp;
        }
}

void main(void)
{
    int values[30], i;
    printf("\n Unsorted list is as follows \n");
    for (i = 0; i < 30; i++)
    {
      values[i] = rand() % 100;
      printf(" %d", values[i]);
    }
    selection_sort(values, 30);

    printf("\n Sorted list is as follows \n");

    for (i = 0; i < 30; i++)
      printf("%d ", values[i]);
}
```

Program 11.

```
/* shell.c */
/* shell sort */
```

(Contd.)

```
#include <stdio.h>
#include <stdlib.h>

void shell_sort(int array[], int size)
{
    int temp, gap, i,swap;

    gap = size / 2;

    do {
      do {
        swap = 0;

        for (i = 0; i < size - gap; i++)
          if (array[i] > array[i + gap])
          {
            temp = array[i];
            array[i] = array[i + gap];
            array[i + gap] = temp;
            swap = 1;
          }
      } while (swap);
    } while (gap = gap / 2);
}

void main(void)
{
    int values[50], i;

    printf("\n Unsorted list is as follows \n");

    for (i = 0; i < 50; i++)
    {
      values[i] = rand() % 100;
      printf(" %d", values[i]);
    }
    shell_sort(values, 50);

    printf("\n Sorted list is as follows \n");

    for (i = 0; i < 50; i++)
      printf("%d ", values[i]);
}
```

Section XI

Program 1.

```
/* addsh.c */

# include<stdio.h>

    char string [10][64] = {
      "a.out"  };
void main()
{
    int i = 1;
    char *arg_ptr[11]; /* Arguments */
    arg_ptr[0] = string[0];
    printf("\n Please enter numbers: ");
    do
    {
      printf("%d: number:",i);
      gets(string[i]);
      if(string[i][0] != '\n')
      arg_ptr[i] = string[i];
else
    arg_ptr[i] = (char *) NULL;
    }
    while(string[i++][0] != '\0' && i < 10);
    printf("-------------");
    if(execvp("a.out", arg_ptr))
                                /* process overlay */
      printf("Error while executing <a.out>\n");
}
```

Program 2.

```
/* break. c */

# include<stdio.h>
# include<signal.h>

int alarm_handler()
{
   printf("\n ****************************** \n");
   printf(" * Have a break have a Kit Kat * \n");
   printf(" ****************************** \n\n");
}

void main(int argc, char *argv[], char *env[])
{
    int time = 2;
    if(argc == 2)
    {
      if((time = atoi (argv[1])) == 0)
        time = 1;
    }

    printf("\n Message appears in %d minutes \n",
    time);
    signal(SIGALRM, alarm_handler);
    alarm(time*60);
    pause();
}
```

Program 3.

```
/* change.c */
# include<stdio.h>

void main()
{
    char ch;
    while((ch=getchar()) != EOF)
    {
      if(islower(ch))
        ch = toupper(ch);
```

(Contd.)

```
        putchar(ch);
      }
    }
```

Program 4.

```
/* getkey.c */
/* This program segment demonstrates terminal
control with the help of function ioctl()
function */

# include<signal.h>
# include<termio.h>

# define MAX_KEY 5

struct termio new, old; /* this gives argument to
ioctl() function */

/* Prototypes */

int sig_handle();
int tty_raw();
int restore_tty();
int getkey(char *);

/* Function main */

void main()
{
    char buffer[MAX_KEY];
                          /* buffer for read a char */
    int x_in;             /* Number of read char */
    int i;                /* index counter */

    if(tty_raw() - 1)
      exit(1);
    do
    {
      x_in = getkey(buffer);
      for (i = 0; i< x_in ; i++)
        printf(" (%d)", buffer[i]);
```

(Contd.)

```
    printf("\n");
   }while((buffer[0] != '\r') && (buffer[0] !=
   '\n'));
   restore_tty();
}

   /* Function tty_raw() sets the terminal
      in raw mode */

int tty_raw()
{
   signal(SIGINT, sig_handle);
   signal(SIGQUIT, sig_handle);
   if(ioctl(0, TCGETA, &old) == -1)
     return (-1);

   new = old ;
   new.c_lflag &= -ICANON; /* raw mode */
   new.c_lflag &= -ECHO; /* echo off */
   new.c_cc[VMIN] = 1; /* individual character */
   new.c_cc[VTIME] = 0; /* no timer */
   return (ioctl(0, TCSETAF, &new));
}

/* This function reset terminal interruption */

int sig_handle()
{
   ioctl(0, TCSETAF, &old);
       exit(0);
}

/* Restore terminal in old state */

int restore_tty()
{
   return (ioctl (0, TCSETAF, &old));
}

/* getkey function reads one character at a time */
/* return number of character read from terminal */
```

(Contd.)

```
int getkey(char *buffer)
{
    return(read(0, buffer, MAX_KEY));
}
```

Program 5.

```
/* input.c */

# include<stdio.h>

void main()
{
    char ch;
    while((ch=getchar()) != EOF)
      putchar(ch);
}
```

Program 6.

```
/* msgrcv.c */
/* This program segment receives message
    from queue */
# ifndef MSG_DEF
# define MSG_DEF

struct msgdata
{
    long typ;
    char buf[512];
};
# endif

# include<sys/ipc.h>
# include<sys/msg.h>
# include<stdio.h>
# include<stdlib.h>
# include<sys/types.h>
# include<sys/shm.h>

/* create a message */
```

(Contd.)

```
int msg_creat(key_t key, int mode)
{
   return(msgget(key, mode | IPC_CREAT |
   IPC_EXCL));
}

/* make a connection */

int msg_attach(key_t key, int mode)
{
   return(msgget(key, mode));
}

/* Receive message function */

int msg_receive (int id, long type, char *buffer)
{
   struct msgdata message;
   int x_read;

   if((x_read = msgrcv(id, &message, BUFSIZ, type,
   0)) < 0)
     return(-1);
   else
   {
     memcpy(buffer, message.buf, x_read);
     return(0);
   }
}

void main(int argc, char *argv[])
{
   key_t key; /* key */

   int msg_id; /* ipd decriptor */

   long msg_type; /* message type */

   char inbuf[BUFSIZ]; /* input buffer */

   char outbuf[BUFSIZ]; /* output buffer */
```

(Contd.)

```
    key_t msg_key;
    if(argc != 3)
    {
      printf("message send failure \n");
      exit(1);
    }

    key = atol(argv[1]);
    msg_type = atol(argv[2]);

    /* Establish connection to message queue */

    if((msg_id = msg_attach(key, 0)) < 0)
    {
      printf("\n Message queue does not exist\n");
      exit(1);
    }

    /* Receive message from the queue */
    msg_receive(msg_id, msg_type, outbuf);

    /* Received message is */
    printf("\n Message received \n");
    puts(outbuf);
}
```

Program 7.

```
/*  msgend.c */

# ifndef MSG_DEF
# define MSG_DEF

struct msgdata
{
    long typ;
    char buf[512];
};
# endif

# include<sys/ipc.h>
# include<sys/msg.h>
```

(Contd.)

```
# include<stdio.h>
# include<stdlib.h>
# include<sys/types.h>
# include<sys/shm.h>
# include<string.h>

/* create a message */

int msg_creat(key_t key, int mode)
{
    return(msgget(key, mode | IPC_CREAT |
    IPC_EXCL));
}

/* make a connection */

int msg_attach(key_t key, int mode)
    {
    return(msgget(key, mode));
    }

/* Send mesage */

int msg_send(int id, long typ, char *buffer, int
size)
{
    struct msgdata message; /* message strcuture */

    message.typ = typ;
    memcpy(message.buf, buffer, size);
    return(msgsnd(id, &message, size, 1));
}

void main(int argc, char *argv[])
{
    key_t key; /* key */

    int msg_id; /* ipd decriptor */

    long msg_type; /* message type */

    char inbuf[BUFSIZ]; /* input buffer */
```

(Contd.)

```
    char outbuf[BUFSIZ]; /* output buffer */

    key_t msg_key;

    msg_type = atol(argv[2]);

    key = atol(argv[1]);

    /* Establish connection with message queue */

    if((msg_id = msg_attach(key, 0)) < 0)
    {
      printf("\n Message queue does not exists \n");
      exit(1);
    }

    /* Data input */

    printf("\n Input information: ");
    gets(inbuf);

    /* Send message */

    if(msg_send(msg_id, msg_type, inbuf,
    strlen(inbuf)) == -1)
      printf("\n Error while sending message \n");
    else
      printf("\n Message sent \n");

}
```

Program 8.

```
/* noquit.c */

# include<stdio.h>
# include<signal.h>

int int_hander();

void main()
{
```

(Contd.)

```
    char buffer [128];
    signal(SIGINT, int_hander);
    signal(SIGQUIT, SIG_IGN);
    for(; ;)
    {
      printf("input>");
      gets(buffer);
      printf("%s\n", buffer);
    }
}

int int_hander()
{
    printf("\n Leave program? (y/n): ");
    if (getchar() != 'n')
      exit(0);
    signal(SIGINT, int_hander);
}
```

Program 9.

```
/* npipe.c */

# include<stdio.h>
# include<stdlib.h>
# include<sys/types.h>
# include<sys/stat.h>
# include<ctype.h>

void main()
{
    int ch;
    FILE *r_pipe, *w_pipe;
    int flag;

    /* creating pipe */

    if(mknod("pipeline", S_IFIFO | 0660, 0) == -1)
    {
      printf("\n Pipe creating error \n");
      exit(1);
    }
```

(Contd.)

```
/* creating first child process */
switch(fork())
{
case -1:
  printf("\n Process generation error \n");
  exit(2);
  break;

  /* first child waiting process */
case 0:
  if((w_pipe = fopen("pipeline", "w"))
  == (FILE *) NULL)
  {
    printf("\n Error while opening the pipe
    \n");
    exit(1);
  }
  while((ch = getchar()) != EOF)
    fputc(ch, w_pipe);
  fclose(w_pipe);
  break;

default:

  /* creating second child process */
  switch(fork())
  {
  case -1:
    printf("\n Second process generation error
    \n");
    break;

    /* second child reading process */

  case 0:
    if((r_pipe = fopen("pipeline", "r")) ==
    (FILE *) NULL)
    {
      printf("\n Error while opening the file
      pipeline");
      exit(1);
    }
```

(Contd.)

```
        while(!feof(r_pipe))
        {
          if(islower(ch = fgetc(r_pipe)))
            ch = toupper(ch);
          putchar(ch);
        }
        fclose(r_pipe);
        break;

      default:
        /* parent process */
        wait(&flag);
                    /* wait for both the children */
        wait(&flag);
        break;
      }
      break;
    }
}
```

Program 10.

```
/* parallel.c */

# include<stdio.h>

void main()
{
    int parent_pid; /* Parent process ID */
    int child_pid ; /* Child process ID */

    switch (fork()) /* process generation */
    {
    case -1: /* Error */
      printf("\n New process not generated \n");
      break;
    case 0:
      child_pid = getpid(); /* child process */
      printf("\nThis is the child PID: %d \n",
      child_pid);
      work(child_pid);
      break;
```

(Contd.)

```
defualt:
      parent_pid = getpid(); /* Parent process */
      printf("\n Parent process PID is: %d",
parent_pid);

      /* Process id printing function */
      work(parent_pid);
      break;
    }
}
int work(int pid)
{
    int i;
    for(i = 0; i < 256; i++)
      printf(" %d", pid);
}
```

Program 11.

```
/* pipe.c */

# include<stdio.h>
# include<stdlib.h>

void main()
{
    int fd[2]; /* file descriptor for pipe */
    int flag;

    /* creating pipe */

    if(pipe(fd) == -1)
    {
      printf("\n Pipe creating error \n");
      exit(1);
    }

    /* creating first child process */
    switch(fork())
    {
    case -1:
      printf("\n Process generation error \n");
```

(Contd.)

```
  exit(2);
  break;

  /* first chile waiting process */
case 0:
  close(1); /* stdout close */

  dup(fd[1]); /* stdout on pipe */
  close(fd[0]); /* pipe read side close*/

  /* overlay process */
  execlp("input", "input", (char *) NULL);
  printf("\n Error during process overlay \n");
  break;
default:

  /* creating second child process */
  switch(fork())
  {
  case -1:
    printf("\n Second process generation error
    \n");
    break;

    /* second child reading process */

  case 0:
    close(0); /* stdin close */

    dup(fd[0]); /* stdin of pipe */
    close(fd[1]); /* pipe/close write side */

    /* overlay process */
    execlp("change", "change", (char *) NULL);
    printf("\n Error during second process
    overlay \n");
    break;
  default:
    /* parent process */
    close(fd[0]); /* close both pipe sides */
    close(fd[1]);
    wait(&flag);
```

(Contd.)

```
/* wait for both the children */
        wait(&flag);
        break;
      }
     break;
    }
}
```

Program 12.

```
/* pwdgrp.c */

# include<unistd.h>
# include<string.h>
# include<pwd.h>
# include<grp.h>
# include<stdio.h>
# define NAM_MAX 16
# define R_UID 0 /* Real user ID */
# define E_UID 1 /* Effetive user ID */
# define R_GID 2 /* Real group ID */
# define E_GID 3 /* Effective group ID */
struct passwd *getpwid();
struct group *gr_ent; /* Entry in group */

/* Function main */

void main()
{
    unsigned short int id[4]; /* IDs */
    char name[4][NAM_MAX]; /* Names */
    struct passwd *pw_ent; /* Entry in password */

    struct group *gr_ent; /* Entry in group */

    int i;

    id[R_UID] = geteuid();
    id[E_UID] = geteuid();
    id[R_GID] = getgid();
    id [E_GID] = getegid();

    for (i =0; i<E_UID; i++)
```

(Contd.)

```
{
  if((pw_ent = getpwuid(id[i])) != (struct
  passwd *) NULL)
    strcpy(name[i], pw_ent->pw_name);
}

for (i = 2; i < E_GID; i++) /* Group name */
{
  if((gr_ent = getgrgid (id[i])) != (struct
  passwd *) NULL)
    strcpy(name[i], gr_ent->gr_name);
}

printf("\n User details \n");
printf("Real user UID: (%d) name: %s\n",
id[R_UID], name[R_UID]);
printf("\n Effective user UID: (%d) Name:
%s\n", id[E_UID], name[E_UID]);
printf("\n Group information \n");

printf("\n Real GID: (%d) Name: %s \n",
id[R_GID], name[R_GID]);
printf("\n Effective GID: (%d) Name: %s \n",
id[E_GID], name[E_GID]);
}
```

Program 13.

```
/* semcreat.c */

# include<sys/ipc.h>
# include<sys/msg.h>
# include<stdio.h>
# include<stdlib.h>
# include<sys/types.h>
# include<sys/shm.h>
# include<sys/sem.h>

/* creating semaphore set */

int sem_creat(key_t key, int num, ushort init, int
mode)
```

(Contd.)

```
{
    int id;
    union semun {
      int val;
      struct semid_ds *buf;
      ushort *array } arg;
    int i;

    /* create semaphore */

    if((id = semget(key, num,
    mode|IPC_CREAT|IPC_EXCL)) < 0)
      return (-1);

    /* Initialise values set */
    for(i=0; i < num; i++)
      arg.array[i] = init;

    /* activate initialization */
    semctl(id, 0, SETALL, arg.array);
    return(id);
}

/* Establish connection to existing semaphore */

int sem_attach(key_t key, int num, int mode)
{
    return(semget(key, num, mode));
}

void main(int argc, char *argv[])
{
    key_t sem_key;
    int sem_id;

    if(argc != 2)
    {
      printf("\n Semphore key values not provided
      properly");
      exit(1);
    }
```

(Contd.)

```
    sem_key = atol(argv[1]);

    /* create semaphore */

    if((sem_id = sem_creat(sem_key, 5, 1, 0666))<0)
      printf("None");
    else
      printf("\n ID: %d", sem_id);
    printf("\n Semaphore created ");
}
```

Program 14.

```
/* semstat.c */

# include<stdio.h>
# include<sys/sem.h>
# include<sys/ipc.h>

int status();
int lst_val();

/* Establish connection to existing semaphore */

int sem_attach(key_t key, int num, int mode)
{
        return(semget(key, num, mode));
}

int sem_stat(int id, struct semid_ds *info)
{
    return(semctl(id, 0, IPC_STAT, info));
}
int sem_values(int id, ushort *values)
{
    struct semid_ds info;
    if(semctl(id, 0, GETALL, values) < 0)
      return(-1);
    else
      return(info.sem_nsems);
}
```

(Contd.)

```
sem_remove(int id)
{
    return(semctl(id, 0, IPC_RMID, 9));
}

/* Function main */

void main(int argc, char *argv[])
{
    key_t key;
    int sem_id;
    if(argc != 3)
    {
      printf("semctl evaluate operations:\n");
      printf("\n s: status");
      printf("\n v: values");
      printf("\n r: Remove");
    }

    /* key and determine ipc descriptor */
    key = atol(argv[1]);
    if((sem_id = sem_attach(key, 5, 0)) < 0)
    {
      printf("Semaphore not found ");
      exit(1);
    }

    switch(argv[1][0])
    {
    case 's':
      status (sem_id);
      break;
    case 'v':
      lst_val(sem_id); /* values inquiry */
          break;
    case 'r':
      if(sem_remove(sem_id) < 0)
        printf("\n Semaphore not deleted \n");
      else
        printf("\n semaphore deleted \n");
      break;
    }
}
```

(Contd.)

```
/* Function status for inquiry semaphore */
int status(int id)
{
    /* id is ipc descriptor */
    struct semid_ds info; /* info structure */
    if(sem_stat(id, &info) < 0)
    {
      printf("\n No status information ");
      return;
    }
    printf("\n Status information \n");
    printf("\n Key: %d", info.sem_perm.key);

    printf("Created by UID %d GID %d",
    info.sem_perm.cuid, info.sem_perm.cgid);
    printf("Owner: UID %d GID %d",
    info.sem_perm.uid, info.sem_perm.gid);
    printf("\n Access rights %o4 \n",
    info.sem_perm.mode &0777);
    printf("\n Number of semaphores %d",
    info.sem_nsems);
}

int lst_val(int id)
{
    ushort val[25]; /* vector fro values */
    int nsems; /* number of semaphores */
    int i;
    /* read entries */
    if((nsems = sem_values(id, val)) < 1)
    {
      printf("\n No entries ");
      return;
    }
    printf("\n Semaphore values \n");
    for(i =0; i < nsems; i++);
    printf("\n Number %d: %d \n", i, val[i]);
}
```

Program 15.

```
/* tcout.c */

# include<curses.h>
# include<term.h>

# ifndef TERMINFO_DEF
# define TERMINFO_DEF

# define TERM_CLS term_code [0] /* erase screen */
# define TERM_CMV term_code [1]
                          /* cursor positioning */
# define TERM_NOR term_code [2] /* normal output */
# define TERM_INV term_code [3]
                          /* inverted output */

/* Screen attributes */

# define NOR 0 /* Normal */
# define INV 1 /* inverted output */

/* error codes */

# define T_NOENV   1 /* &TERN not set     */
# define T_NOENTRY 2 /* no entry in termcap */
# define T_NODES   3
                 /* no description for features */

/* prototypes */

# endif

static char termbuf[1024];
static char codebuf[1024];
static char *term_code[4];
static int max_lin =24;
static int max_col = 80;
int term_err = 0;
char code_name[4][4] = {
   "cl","cm","se","so"};
```

(Contd.)

```
/* Read and interpret the termcap description $TERM
must be defined */

int read_term()
{
    char *t_name;
    char *ptr;
    extern char *getenv(), *tgetstr();
    int i;

    /* Terminal name from environment */

    if (t_name = getenv("TERM")) == (char *) NULL)
    {
      term_err = T_NOENV;
      return(-1);

      /* Read the termcap entry */

      if(tgetent(termbuf, t_name) == -1)
      {
        term_err = T_NOENTRY;
        return(-1);
      }
      /* Determine screen columns and rows */

      ptr = codebuf;

      if(((max_col == tgetnum("co")) == -1)))
        ((max_lin = tgetnum("li")) == -1))
          {
          term_err = T_NODES;
          return(-1);
        }

      /* Read and decode control sequences */
      for(i = 0; i < 4; i++)
      {
        term_code[i] = tgetstr(code_name[i], &ptr);
        if(term_code[i] == (char *) NULL)
        {
          term_err = T_NODES;
```

(Contd.)

```
            return (-1);
          }
        }
      return (0);
    }

    /* output function */

    int outp(char ch)
    {
      write(1, &ch, 1);
    }

    /* output of a string */

    int print_str(char *text)
    {
      while(*text != '\0')
        outp(*text++);
    }

    /* set the screen attributes */
    int set_color(int color)
    {
      if(color == NOR)
        tputs(TERM_NOR, 1, outp);
      else if(color == INV)
        tputs(TERM_INV, 1, outp);
    }

/* The gotoxy function sets the cursor position */

    int gotoxy(int xpos, int ypos)
    {
      extern char *tparm ();
      tputs(tgoto(TERM_CMV, ypos, xpos), 1, outp);
    }

    /* Clear the screen */

    int cl_screen()
    {
```

(Contd.)

```
  tputs(TERM_CLS, 1, outp);
}

/* Draw box */

int frame(int x1, int y1, int x2, int y2)
{
  int i;
  gotoxy(x1, y1);
  outp('+');
  for(i = (x1+1); i <= x2; i++)
    outp('-');
  outp('+');
  for(i = (y1+1); i < y2; i++)
  {
    gotoxy(x1, i);
    outp('!');
    gotoxy(x2, i);
    outp('!');
  }
  gotoxy(x1, y2);
  outp('+');
  for(i = (x1+1); i <= x2; i++)
    outp('-');
  outp('+');
}

/* Main function */

void main()
{
  if (read_term() - 1)
  {
    printf("\n Error while reading /etc/termcap
    \n");
    exit(-1);
  }

  cl_screen();
  frame(1, 0, max_col-2, max_lin-1);
  set_color(INV);
  gotoxy(32,0);
```

(Contd.)

```
        print_str("TITLE");
        set_color(NOR);
        gotoxy(3,1);
        print_str("First Row");
        gotoxy(3,2);
        print_str("Draw");
        printf("\n Press a key to clear the screen:"),
        getchar();
        cl_screen();
      }
```

Program 16.

```
/* tiout.c */

# include<curses.h>
# include<term.h>

# ifndef TERMINFO_DEF
# define TERMINFO_DEF

/* Screen attributes */

# define NOR 0 /* Normal */
# define INV 1 /* inverted output */

/* error codes */

# define T_NOENV 1 /* normal not set */
# define T_NODES 3 /* no entry */

/* prototypes */

# endif


int init_term()
{
        int err; /* Error message */
        setupterm ((char *) NULL, 1, & err);
        if(err != 1)
                return (T_NOENV);
```

(Contd.)

```
        if(columns < 1 || lines < 1)
                return(T_NODES);
        if(enter_standout_mode == (char*) NULL)
                return (T_NODES);
        if(cursor_address == (char *) NULL)
                return(T_NODES);
        if(clear_screen == (char *) NULL)
                return(T_NODES);
         return(0);
}

int outp(char ch)
{
   write(1, &ch, 1);
}

int print_str(char *text)
{
        while(*text != '\0')
                outp(*text++);
}

int set_color(int color)
{
        if(color == NOR)
          tputs(exit_standout_mode, 1, outp);
        else if(color == INV)
            tputs(enter_standout_mode, 1, outp);
}

/* gotoxy */

int gotoxy(int xpos, int ypos)
{
     extern char *tparm ();
     tputs(tparm(cursor_address, ypos, xpos), 1,
      outp);
}
int cl_screen()
{
        tputs(clear_screen, 1, outp);
}
```

(Contd.)

```
/* Draw box */

int frame(int x1, int y1, int x2, int y2)
{
        int i;
        gotoxy(x1, y1);
        outp('+');
        for(i = (x1+1); i < x2; i++)
                outp('-');
        outp('+');
        for(i = (y1+1); i < y2; i++)
        {
                gotoxy(x1, i);
                outp('!');
                gotoxy(x2, i);
                outp('!');
        }
        gotoxy(x1, y2-1);
        outp('+');
        for(i = (x1+1); i < x2; i++)
                outp('-');
        outp('+');
}

/* Main function */

void main()
{
        if (init_term());
        cl_screen();
        frame(1, 0, columns-2, lines-1);
        set_color(INV);
        gotoxy(32,0);
        print_str("TITLE");
        set_color(NOR);
        gotoxy(3,1);
        print_str("First Row");
        gotoxy(3,10);
   print_str("Draw");
   getchar();
   cl_screen();
   resetterm();
```

Program 17.

```
/* wait.c */

# include<stdio.h>
# include<stdlib.h>

void main()
{
    int status;
    printf("\n Parent process is waiting for child
    process! ");
    switch(fork())
    {
    case -1:
      printf("\n Error during process generation!
      \n");
      exit(1);
      break;

    case 0:
      if(execlp("ps", "ps", "-el", (char *) NULL))
      {
        printf("Error during process overlay! \n");
        exit(1);
      }
      break;
    default:
      wait(&status);
      printf("\n Child process ended with status
      \n");
      printf("\n Low order bit: %o4", status &
      0xff);
      printf("\n high order bit: %o4 \n", status >>
      8);
      break;
    }
}
```

Section XII

Program 1.

```
/* dbase.c */

/**************************************************/
/***  Database design using doubly linked list ***/
/**************************************************/

# include<stdio.h>
# include<string.h>
# include<malloc.h>
# include<stdlib.h>

/* struct definition */

struct addr
{
        char name[120];
        char roll[30];
        char branch[40];
        char year[5];
        char address[200];

        struct addr *next ;
        struct addr *prior ;
};

struct addr list_entry ;
struct addr *start ;
struct addr *last ;
```

(Contd.)

```
/* Global declaration of variables */

int choice ;
int i = 0 , n ;

/*  Prototype of function used in this program
segment */

void  gets1(char *);   /* This is function used to
                            read data */
void  main_menu();     /* This function displays
                            menu */
void  input();         /* This function supplied
                            data to the program */
void load();           /* This function load the
                            database file */
void store();        /* This function stores the
                          information into a file */
void list();  /* This function shows the list of
      records available in the database  file */

void delete ();   /* This deletes a record from
                    database file */
void update () ; /* This function is used to update
           infromation associated with a record */
void search();     /* This function is used to
                        search for a record */

void printer(); /* This function valid only
          superuser for generation of hardcopy of
          the list of the records*/

/* End of prototype  */

/* function main */

void  main()
{

        while(1)

        {
```

(Contd.)

```
system("clear");
main_menu(); /* menu function */
choice = getchar();
choice = toupper(choice);

switch(choice)
 {

case 'L':
 getchar();
 load();
 printf("FILE SUCCESSFUL LOADED ");
 printf("\nPress A key ");
 getchar();
 break;

case 'I':
 getchar();
 printf("\nINPUT  SESSION ");
 printf("\n Press a key");
 getchar();
 input();
 break;

case 'T':
 getchar();
 printf("\nLISTING  SESSION ");
 printf("\n Press a key");
 getchar();
 list();
 getchar();
 break ;

case 'U':
 getchar();
 update();
 getchar();
 break;

case 'D':

 getchar();
```

(Contd.)

```
                  delete();
                  getchar();
                  break;

                 case 'S':
                  search();
                  break;

                 case 'E':
                  printf("\nEND OF SESSION ");
                  printf("\n Press a key");
                  getchar();
                  exit(0);

                 case 'P':
                  getchar();
                  printf("\n Hard copy generating");
                  printer();
                  getchar();
                  }
        }
}

/* end of function main */

/* function input */

void  input()
{
        struct addr *info, *find() ;
        FILE *fp;
        fp=fopen("rec.dat","r");
        if(fp!=NULL)
                load();
        do
        {
                info = malloc(sizeof(list_entry));
                if ( info == 0 )
                {
                        printf("\n OUT OF MEMORY");
                        exit(0);
                }
```

(Contd.)

```
printf("\n\n Type 'end' when finished");
      printf("\nEnter Roll Number: ");
      gets1(info->roll);

      if(strcmp(info->roll,"end")==0)
            break;
      if(!(info = find(info->roll)))
      {
         printf("\nEnter Name : ");
         gets1(info->name);

         printf("\nEnter Branch: ");
         gets1(info->branch);

         printf("\nEnter year: ");
         gets1(info->year);

         printf("\nEnter Address : ");
         gets1(info->address);
      }
      else
      {
  printf("\n This record already exist");
      }
      if ( start != 0 )
      {
            last->next = info ;
            info->prior = last ;
            last = info ;
            last->next = 0;
      }

      else
      {
            start = info ;
            start->next = 0 ;
            last  = start ;
            start->prior = 0;
      }

} while(1);
store ();
```

(Contd.)

```
}
/* end of input function */

/* store function */

void store ()
{
        register int t , size ;
        struct  addr  *info ;
        char *p ;
        FILE *fp;
        fp = fopen ("rec.dat","w");
        if(fp == NULL)
         {
                printf("File rec.dat \n");
                perror("ERROR  : ");
                exit(0);
         }

        size = sizeof(list_entry);
        info = start ;
        while(info)
         {
                p =(char *) info ;
                for( t = 0 ; t < size ;  ++t)
                        putc(*p++,fp);
                info = info->next;
         }
        putc(EOF,fp);
        fclose(fp);
}

/* end of function store */

/* load function */

void load ( )
{
        register int t , size ;
        struct  addr  *info, *temp ;
        char *p ;
        FILE *fp;
```

(Contd.)

```
        fp = fopen ("rec.dat","r");
        if(fp == NULL)
        {
                printf("DATA BASE FILE DOS NOT
                EXIST-> rec.dat \n");
                perror("ERROR  : ");
                exit(0);
        }

        size = sizeof(list_entry);
        start = malloc(size);
        if(!start)
        {
                printf("\n Out Of Memmory ");
        }

        info = start ;
        p =(char *) info ;

        while((*p++ = getc(fp)) != EOF)
        {
                for( t = 0 ; t < size - 1 ;  ++t)
                        *p++ = getc(fp) ;
                info->next = malloc(size);
                if ( !info->next)
                {
                        printf("\n Out of Memory ");
                        break ;
                }
                info->prior = temp ;
                temp = info ;
                info = info->next ;
                p =(char *) info ;
        }
        free(temp->next);
        temp->next = 0 ;
        last = temp ;
        start->prior = 0 ;
        fclose(fp);
}

/* End of load function */
```

(Contd.)

```
/* function list */

void  list ()
{

        int i = 1 , j = 1 ;
        register int t ;
        struct addr *info ;
        info = start ;
        if(!info)
                printf("\n load file ");
        while(info)
        {
                display(info);
                info =info->next ;

/* Show 5 Records at a time on the screen */
                if (i  ==  5*j)
                {
                   printf("\n Press any key to
                   continue ");
                   getchar();
                   j ++ ;
                   i ++ ;
                }
                i++;
                printf("\n\n");
        }
}

/* end of list function */

/* display function */

display(info)

struct addr *info ;
{
        printf("\n Roll Number: %s", info->roll);
        printf("\n Name        : %s", info->name);
        printf("\n Branch      : %s", info->branch);
        printf("\n Year        : %s", info->year);
```

(Contd.)

```
        printf("\n Address : %s", info->address);

        return ;
}

/*  end of display function */

/* delete function */

void  delete( )
{
        char Roll[20];
        register int t , size ;
        struct  addr  *info, *find() ;
        printf("\nDELETION SESSION ");
        printf("\n Press a key");
        getchar();

        printf("\n Enter Roll Number of the record
         you want to delete: ");
        gets1(Roll);
        info = find(Roll);

        if(info)
        {
                if(start== info )
                {
                        start = info->next ;
                        start->prior = 0;
                }
                else
                {
                  info->prior->next = info->next ;
                  if(info != last)
                        {
                  info->next->prior = info->prior ;
                        }
                        else
                        {
                  last = info->prior ;
                        }
                }
```

(Contd.)

```
                    free(info);
                    store() ;
                     printf("\n Record successfully
                    deleted ");
        }
        else
                    printf("\n Record  not found ");
}

/* End of delete function */

/* search function */

void  search()
{
        char Roll[20];
        struct addr *info, *find();
        printf("\n SEARCH SESSION ");
        printf("\n Press a key");
        getchar();

        printf("\n Enter Roll of the record you
         want to find: ");
        gets1(Roll);
        if(!(info = find(Roll)))
        {
                    printf("\n Record does not exist");
                    printf("\n Press a key");
                    getchar();
        }
        else
        {
                    display(info) ;
                    printf("\n Press a key");
                    getchar();
        }

}
/* End of function search */

/* Function find */
```

(Contd.)

```
struct addr *find(Roll)
char *Roll;
{
        struct addr *info ;
        info = start ;

        while(info)
         {
                 if(strcmp(info->roll, Roll)== 0 )
                         return( info);
                info = info->next ;
         }
        return 0 ;

}

/* End of find function */

/* Function update */

void update ()
{
        char Roll[20];
        char choice;
        struct addr *info;

        printf("\n Enter Roll Number : ");
        gets1(Roll);
        info = start  ;
        while(info)
         {
                 if(strcmp(info->roll, Roll) == 0 )
                  {
                         display(info) ;
                          /*
                      if(strcmp(info->name, "end")==0)
                          break ; */
                printf("\n NEW RECORD for: %s ",Roll);
                printf("\n Name: %s", info->name);
                printf("\n You want update this field
                  (y/n): ");
                         choice = getchar();
```

(Contd.)

```
choice = toupper(choice);
fflush(stdin);
if(choice == 'Y')
    {
   printf("\n Enter Name : ");
fflush(stdin);
gets1(info->name);
fflush(stdin);
    }
   printf("\n Roll Number: %s", info-
    >roll);
   printf("\n You want update this
    field (y/n): ");
choice = getchar();
choice = toupper(choice);
fflush(stdin);
if(choice == 'Y')
    {
   printf("\n Enter Roll Number: ");
fflush(stdin);
gets1(info->roll);
fflush(stdin);
    }
   printf("\n Branch: %s", info-
    >branch);
   printf("\n You want update this
    field (y/n): ");
choice = getchar();
choice = toupper(choice);
fflush(stdin);
if(choice == 'Y')
    {
   printf("\n Enter Branch: ");
fflush(stdin);
gets1(info->branch);
fflush(stdin);
    }
   printf("\n Year: %s", info->year);
   printf("\n You want update this
 field (y/n): ");
choice = getchar();
choice = toupper(choice);
```

(Contd.)

```
                    fflush(stdin);
                    if(choice == 'Y')
                         {
                         printf("\n Enter year: ");
                    fflush(stdin);
                    gets1(info->year);
                    fflush(stdin);
                         }
                         printf("\n Address: %s",
                         info->address);
                        printf("\n You want update
                         this field (y/n): ");
                    choice = getchar();
                    choice = toupper(choice);
                    fflush(stdin);
                    if(choice == 'Y')
                         {
                     printf("\n Enter Address : ");
                     fflush(stdin);
                     gets1(info->address);
                     fflush(stdin);

                         }
                     store () ;
                }
                else
                {
                    printf(" No More Record is
                    found: %s",Roll);

                    printf("\n Press a key");
                }

               info = info->next ;
        }
}

/* End of update function */

/* Function menu */

void  main_menu()
```

(Contd.)

```
{
        int i ;
        char *string[] ={
                        "L-> LOAD ",
                        "I-> INPUT ",
                        "T-> LIST  ",
                        "U-> UPDATE",
                        "D-> DELETE",
                        "S-> SEARCH",
                        "P-> Report",
                        "E-> EXIT",
                        " Enter your choice: "
                        };

         for( i = 0 ; i <= 8 ; i++)
        {
                printf("\n %s",string[i]);
        }
}

/* Definition of function gets1() */

void gets1(char *s)
{
        int i ;
        char ch ;
        i = 0 ;
        ch = getchar() ;
        while(ch != '\n')
        {
                s[i] = ch ;
                i ++ ;
                ch = getchar() ;
        }
        s[i] = '\0' ;
}

/* Hard copy generating function */
/* This function valid only in superuser mode */

void printer()
{
```

(Contd.)

```
    FILE *fp1;
    int i = 1 , j = 1 ;
    register int t ;
    struct addr *info ;
    info = start ;
    if(!info)
            printf("\n load file ");

    fp1 = fopen("/dev/lp0", "w");

    if(fp1 == NULL)
    {
            perror("\n Error: ");
            return;
    }


    while(info)
    {
fprintf(fp1, "\n Roll Number: %s",info->roll);
fprintf(fp1, "\n Name        : %s",info->name);
fprintf(fp1, "\n Branch      : %s", info-
>branch);
fprintf(fp1, "\n Year        : %s", info-
>year);
fprintf(fp1, "\n Address     : %s",info-
>address);

            info =info->next ;

/* Show 5 Records at a time on the screen */
            if (i  ==  5*j)
            {
    printf("\n Press any key to continue ");
                    getchar();
                    j ++ ;
                    i ++ ;
            }
            i++;
            printf("\n\n");
```

Program 2.

```
/* LEXICAL.C */
/******************************************/
/**********    LEXICAL ANALYZER    *********/
/******************************************/

# include<stdio.h>
# include<string.h>
# include<ctype.h>

void main()
{

        /* Key word of 'C' language */

        static char *KEYWORD[43]={

"asm",       "auto",        "break",       "case",
"cdecl",     "char",        "const",       "continue",
"default",   "do",          "double",      "else",
"enum",      "extern",      "far",         "float",
"for",       "goto",        "huge",        "if",
"int",       "interrupt",   "long",        "near",
"pascal",    "register",    "return",      "short",
"signed",    "sizeof",      "static",      "struct",
"switch",    "typedef",     "union",       "unsigned",
"void",      "volatile",    "while",       "_cs",
"_ds",       "_es",         "_ss"
                            };

        static char BREAK1[31]=" -~!&*,;/%+<>^|?:=
        (){}[].\n\t\f\v\b";
        /*  List of variables */

        FILE *FS,*FU;
        char token[50], brk[50], *chk, file[50];
        char ch, d;

        /* Prototype of functions */

        int  CHKLIT(char *);
```

(Contd.)

```
char *CHKOP(char *);

/* Initializations */

int i=0 ;
int k=0 ;
int b=0 ;
int t=0 ;
int lt=0 ;
int com=0 ;
int ck=0 ;
int u=1 ;
int squote=0 ;
int dquote=0 ;

/* End of declaration portion */

system("clear");

printf("\n ENTER FILE NAME: ");
gets(file);
system("clear");

FS=fopen(file,"r");

if( FS == NULL )
{
        printf("\n File: %s", file);
        perror("\n ERROR: ");
        exit(1);
}

FU=fopen("UST.C","w"); /* save output result */

/* * * * * * * * * * * * * * * * * * * * * */

ch = fgetc(FS);
while(ch != EOF)
{
        while(1)
        {
                if(ch == EOF)
                        break;
```

(Contd.)

```
if(ch == '*' && brk[b-1] == '/' && !com && b)
                    {
                            b--;
                            com=1;
                    }
                   if(com==1)
                    {

if(ch == '/' && d == '*')
                            com=0;
                            d = ch;
                            ch = fgetc(FS);
                            continue;
                    }


if(ch == '"')
                    {
if(token[t-1] != '\\' && !squote)
                            {
                            lt++;
dquote = ((dquote == 0) ? 1 : 0);
                            }
if((token[t-1] == '\\' && token[t-2] == '\\')
 && !squote)
                            {
                            lt++;
dquote = ((dquote == 0) ? 1 : 0);
                            }
                    }

                   if(ch == '\'')
                    {
if(token[t-1] != '\\' && !dquote)
                            {
                                    lt++;
 squote = ((squote == 0) ? 1: 0);
                            }
 if((token[t-1] == '\\' && token[t-2] == '\\')
  && !dquote)
                            {
                                    lt++;
```

(Contd.)

```
squote = ((squote == 0) ? 1 : 0);
                        }
                }

if(!lt)
  for(i = 0; i < 31; i++)
if(ch == BREAK1[i])
break;


if(i != 31 && !lt)
                {
brk[b] = ch;
                    b++;
                }

if(i == 31 || lt)
                {
if(t && b)
break;
  token[t] = ch;
  t++;
  b = 0;
                }
 if(lt == 2)
    lt=0;
    ch = fgetc(FS);
    }
/* * * * * * * * * * * * * * * * */

    token[t] = '\0';
    t = 0;
    brk[b] ='\0';
    b = 0;

if(CHKLIT(token) == 0)
            k = 1;
    else
            k = 0;

    chk = CHKOP(brk);
```

(Contd.)

```
 printf("%-35s%-10d      ",token,u);
fprintf(FU,"%-35s%-10d  ",token,u);
                                  u++;
          if(k == 1)
          {
                  for(i = 0; i < 43; i++)
        if(strcmp(token, KEYWORD[i]) == 0)
                                   break;
                  if(i == 43)
                  {
 printf("IDN\n");
 fprintf(FU,"IDN\n");
                  }
                  else
                  {
  fprintf(FU,"KEYWORD\n");
  printf("KEYWORD\n");
                  }
          }
          if(k == 0)
          {
  printf("LIT\n");
  fprintf(FU,"LIT\n");
          }

          i = 0;
          ck = 0;
          while(chk[i] != '\0')
          {
                  if(chk[i] != ' ')
                  {
  printf("%c",chk[i]);
  fprintf(FU,"%c",chk[i]);
                          ck++;
                          i++;
                          continue;
                  }
                  if(ck == 1)
                  {
  printf("%-34c",' ');
  fprintf(FU,"%-34c",' ');
  if(chk[i-1] == '*' || chk[i-1] == '+' ||
```

(Contd.)

```
chk[i-1] == '-' || chk[i-1] == '/' ||
chk[i-1] == '%' || chk[i-1] == '<' ||
chk[i-1] == '>' || chk[i-1] == '=' ||
chk[i-1] == '!')
                                {
     printf("%-10d     OP\n",u);
    fprintf(FU,"%-10d     OP\n",u);
                                }
                                else
                                {
    printf("%-10d     TRM\n",u);
    fprintf(FU,"%-10d     TRM\n",u);
                                }
                                u++;
                                ck = 0;
                        }
                        if(ck == 2)
                        {
    printf("%-33c",' ');
    fprintf(FU,"%-33c",' ');
    printf("%-10d     D-OP\n",u);
    fprintf(FU,"%-10d     D-OP\n",u);
                                u++;
                                ck = 0;
                        }
                        if(ck == 3)
                        {
    printf("%-33c",' ');
    fprintf(FU,"%-33c",' ');
    printf("%-10d     T-OP\n",u);
    fprintf(FU,"%-10d     T-OP\n",u);
                                u++;
                                ck = 0;
                        }
                        i++;
                }
                if(ck == 1)
                {
    printf("%-34c",' ');
    fprintf(FU,"%-34c",' ');
    if(chk[i-1] == '*' || chk[i-1] == '+' ||
       chk[i-1] == '-' || chk[i-1] == '/' ||
```

(Contd.)

```
chk[i-1] == '%' || chk[i-1] == '<' ||
chk[i-1] == '>' || chk[i-1] == '=' ||
chk[i-1] == '!')
                    {
      printf("%-10d     OP\n",u);
      fprintf(FU,"%-10d     OP\n",u);
                    }
                    else
                    {
      printf("%-10d     TRM\n",u);
      fprintf(FU,"%-10d     TRM\n",u);
                    }
                    u++;
            }
            if(ck == 2)
            {
      printf("%-33c",' ');
      fprintf(FU,"%-33c",' ');
      printf("%-10d     D-OP\n",u);
      fprintf(FU,"%-10d     D-OP\n",u);
                    u++;
            }
            if(ck == 3)
            {
      printf("%-32c",' ');
      fprintf(FU,"%-32c",' ');
      printf("%-10d     T-OP\n",u);
      fprintf(FU,"%-10d     T-OP\n",u);
                    u++;
                    ck = 0;
            }

            getchar();
            token[t] = ch;
            t++;
            ch = fgetc(FS);
      }
      printf("SUCCESS...");
       getchar();


 * The function CHKLIT() check for the literals */
```

(Contd.)

```
int CHKLIT(char *a)
{
        int i = 0,j = 0,k = 1;
        if(a[i] != '"' && a[i] != '\'')
        {
                while(a[i] != '\0')
                {
                  if(isdigit(a[i]) || a[i] == '.')
                        {
                                if(a[i++] == '.')
                                        j++;
                                if(j > 1)
                                {
                                        k = 0;
                                        break;
                                }
                        }
                        else
                        {
                                k = 0;
                                break;
                        }
                }
        }
        return(k);
}

/* This function check for operators */
char *CHKOP(char *a)
{
        char c, d= '\0', e= '\0', f[5], z[50];
        int i = 0, j = 0, l = 0, u;
        char *BREAK2[21]={
"<<",    "[]",    "->",    "++",    "--",

"<<",    ">>",    "<=",    ">=",    "==",

"!=",    "&&",    "||",    "*=",    "/=",

"%=",    "+=",    "-=",    "&=",    "^=",

"|="
                                    };
```

(Contd.)

```
        u = strlen(a);
        c = a[i];
        while(i < u)
        {
if(c == ' '  || c == '\n' || c== '\b' ||
   c == '\t' || c == '\v' || c=='\f')
                {
                        i++;
                        c = a [i];
                        continue;
                }
                if(i)
                {
                        f[0] = e;
                        f[1] = d;
                        f[2] = c;
                        f[3] = '\0';
if(strcmp(f,">>=") == 0 || strcmp(f,"<<=") == 0)
                        {
                           z[l] = c;
                            l++;
                        }
                        else
                        {
                           f[0] = d;
                           f[1] = c;
                           f[2] = '\0';
                           for(j = 0; j < 21; j++)
 if(strcmp(f, BREAK2[j]) == 0)
                                                break;
                                if(j != 21)
                                {
                            z[l] = c;
                            l++;
                                }
                                if(j == 21)
                                {
                            z[l] = ' ';
                            l++;
                            z[l] = c;
                            l++;
                                }
```

(Contd.)

```
                        }
                        e = d;
                        d = c;
                        i++;
                        c = a[i];
                }
                else
                {
                        z[l] = c;
                        d = c;
                        l++;
                        i++;
                        c = a[i];
                }
        }
        z[l] = '\0';
        return(z);
}
```

Program 3.

```
/****************************************/
/**             PRINT.C              **/
/****************************************/
/*      Print service  routines        */
/****************************************/

# include<stdio.h>
# include<stdlib.h>

# define ESC 27

/*  Prototype */

void print_string(char *);
void wide_printer(void);
void condensed_printer(void);
void underlined_printer(void);
void italic_printer(void);
void emphesized_printer(void);
void bold_printer(void);
void elite_printer(void);
```

(Contd.)

```
void pica_printer(void);
void def_mode_printer(void);
void near_printer(void);
void spacing_printer(void);

void menu();

/*      End                */

/* Function main */

void main()
{
        char choice ;

        do
        {
                menu() ;

                choice = getchar();
                choice =  toupper(choice);

                switch(choice)
                {
                case  'W' :
                        wide_printer() ;
                        break ;

                case  'C' :
                        condensed_printer() ;
                        break ;

                case  'U' :
                        underlined_printer() ;
                        break ;

                case  'I' :
                        italic_printer() ;
                        break ;

                case  'E' :
                        emphesized_printer() ;
                        break ;
```

(Contd.)

```
                    case  'B' :
                          bold_printer() ;
                          break ;

                    case  'L' :
                          elite_printer() ;
                          break ;

                    case  'P' :
                          pica_printer() ;
                          break ;

                    case  'D' :
                          def_mode_printer() ;
                          break ;

                    case  'N' :
                          near_printer() ;
                          break ;

                    case  'S' :
                          spacing_printer() ;
                          break ;

                    case 'T' :
                          exit(0);
                          break;
                    default :
                   printf("\n Choice is wrong ");
                          break ;
                    }

                   printf("Press any key to cont..");
                    getchar();
          }  while(choice != 'T');
}

/* Print wide service */

/*********************************************/
/** THIS IS ROUTINE WHICH WILL PRINTS FILES **/
/*********************************************/
```

(Contd.)

```
/* Function wide_printer */

void wide_printer()
{
        char file[13] ;
        int tm, bm, pl;
        int row=0,i,top_of_page=1,r;
        int p=1;
        int ch,j;
        int number;
        int blank;
        int b;
        FILE *fs, *fp1;
        printf("Enter File: ");
        scanf("%s",file);

        fs=fopen(file,"rb"); /* open source file */

        if(fs==NULL)
        {
                printf("%s",file);
                perror("ERROR : ");
                exit(-1);
        }

        fp1=fopen("/dev/lp0","w");
/* open /dev/lp0 system device for print */

        if(fp1==NULL)
        {
                printf("%/dev/lp0");
                perror("ERROR : ");
                exit(-1);
        }

        printf("NUMBER OF COPY: ");
        scanf(" %d",&number);

        tm=6;     /* top margin */
        bm=8;     /* bottom margin */
        pl= 65;   /* page length */
```

(Contd.)

```
        for(j=0;j<number;j++)
         {
                rewind(fs);
        /* Title printing */

        for(i = 0; i< 30; i++)
         putc(' ',fp1);
            /* set position of print head at
                30 column of the paper */

print_string(file); /* print file name as title */

                while((ch=fgetc(fs)) !=EOF)
                 {
                        putc(ESC, fp1);
                        putc(14, fp1);

                        if(top_of_page)
                         {
                         for ( i=0; i<tm; i++)
                                putc('\n',fp1);
                                top_of_page=0;
                         }
                        putc(ch,fp1);
                        if(ch=='\n')
                         {
                                row++;
                        if(row==pl-tm-bm-1)
                                 {
                        for(i=0;i<bm;i++)
                                 {
                         putc('\n',fp1) ;
                                 }

                        for(i = 0; i< 30; i++)
                        putc(' ',fp1);
                    /* set position of print head at
                        30 column of the paper */

                        fprintf(fp1, "%d", p);

                        if(p > 1)
                                        {
```

(Contd.)

```
                fprintf(fp1, "\n");
                fprintf(fp1, "\n");
                              }

                              p++;
                top_of_page=1;
                              row=0;
                         }
                    }
            }
            if(row<(pl-tm-bm))
            /* add blank lines at the bottom */
            {
                 blank = pl - tm - row - 1;
                 for( b=0; b< blank; b++)
                      putc('\n',fp1);

                 for(i = 0; i< 30; i++)
                 putc(' ',fp1);
          /* set position of print head  at 30
            column of the paper */

                 fprintf(fp1,"%d", p);
                 top_of_page=1;
                 row=0;
            }

            p=1;

       }
       putc(20, fp1);
       fclose(fp1);
       fclose(fs);
}

/* End of function printer  */

/* Print string function */

/**************************************************/
/*           Print condensed service            */
```

(Contd.)

```
/*******************************************/
/** THIS IS ROUTINE WHICH WILL PRINTS FILES **/
/*******************************************/

/* Function condensed__printer */

void condensed_printer()
{
        char file[13] ;
        int tm, bm, pl;
        int row=0,i,top_of_page=1,r;
        int p=1;
        int ch,j;
        int number;
        int blank;
        int b;
        FILE *fs, *fp1;
        printf("Enter File: ");
        scanf("%s",file);

        fs=fopen(file,"rb"); /* open source file */

        if(fs==NULL)
        {
                printf("%s",file);
                perror("ERROR : ");
                exit(-1);
        }

        fp1=fopen("/dev/lp0","w"); /* open /dev/lp0
                         system device for print */

        if(fp1==NULL)
        {
                printf("%/dev/lp0");
                perror("ERROR : ");
                exit(-1);
        }


        printf("NUMBER OF COPY: ");
        scanf(" %d",&number);
```

(Contd.)

```
tm=6;      /* top margin */
bm=8;      /* bottom margin */
pl= 65;  /* page length */

for(j=0;j<number;j++)
 {
        rewind(fs);

/* Title printing */

for(i = 0; i< 30; i++)
        putc(' ',fp1);  /* set position of
     print head at 30 column of the paper */

print_string(file);   /* print file name as
                             title */
        while((ch=fgetc(fs)) !=EOF)
         {
                putc(ESC, fp1);
                putc(15, fp1);

                if(top_of_page)
                 {
                    for ( i=0; i<tm; i++)
                       putc('\n',fp1);
                        top_of_page=0;
                 }
                putc(ch,fp1);
                if(ch=='\n')
                 {
                      row++;
                      if(row==pl-tm-bm-1)
                        {
                           for(i=0;i<bm;i++)
                                {
                          putc('\n',fp1) ;
                                }

                     for(i = 0; i< 30; i++)
                     putc(' ',fp1);
           /* set position of print head at
              30 column of the paper */
```

(Contd.)

```
                fprintf(fp1, "%d", p);

                        if(p > 1)
                        {
                fprintf(fp1, "\n");
               fprintf(fp1, "\n");
                         }


                               p++;
                               top_of_page=1;
                               row=0;
                              }
                       }
               }
              if(row<(pl-tm-bm))  /* add blank
                             lines at the bottom */
               {
                 blank = pl - tm - row - 1;
                 for( b=0; b< blank; b++)
                 putc('\n',fp1);

                 for(i = 0; i< 30; i++)
                 putc(' ',fp1);
                /* set position of print head at
                   30 column of the paper */

                      fprintf(fp1, "%d", p);
                      top_of_page=1;
                      row=0;
               }

              p=1;

        }
       putc(18, fp1);
       fclose(fp1);
       fclose(fs);
}

/* End of function printer  */

/* Print string function */
```

(Contd.)

```
/*******************************************/
/*        Print underlined service        */
/*******************************************/
/** THIS IS ROUTINE WHICH WILL PRINTS FILES **/
/*******************************************/
/* Function underlined print services */

 void underlined_printer()
{
       char file[13] ;
       int tm, bm, pl;
       int row=0,i,top_of_page=1,r;
       int p=1;
       int ch,j;
       int number;
       int blank;
       int b;
       FILE *fs, *fp1;
       printf("Enter File: ");
       scanf("%s",file);

       fs=fopen(file,"rb"); /* open source file */

       if(fs==NULL)
       {
              printf("%s",file);
              perror("ERROR : ");
              exit(-1);
       }

       fp1=fopen("/dev/lp0","w");
       /* open /dev/lp0 system device for print */

       if(fp1==NULL)
       {
              printf("%/dev/lp0");
              perror("ERROR : ");
              exit(-1);
       }


       printf("NUMBER OF COPY: ");
```

(Contd.)

```
scanf(" %d",&number);

tm=6;      /* top margin */
bm=8;      /* bottom margin */
pl= 65;  /* page length */

for(j=0;j<number;j++)
 {
        rewind(fs);

/* Title printing */

for(i = 0; i< 30; i++)
        putc(' ',fp1);
           /* set position of print head at
              30 column of the paper */

print_string(file); /* print file name as
                       title */

        while((ch=fgetc(fs)) !=EOF)
         {
                putc(ESC, fp1);
                putc(45, fp1);
                putc(1, fp1);
                if(top_of_page)
                 {
                   for ( i=0; i<tm; i++)
                  putc('\n',fp1);
                     top_of_page=0;
                 }
                putc(ch,fp1);
                if(ch=='\n')
                 {
                    row++;
                   if(row==pl-tm-bm-1)
                    {
                       for(i=0;i<bm;i++)
                           {
                       putc('\n',fp1) ;
                           }
```

(Contd.)

```
            for(i = 0; i< 30; i++)
             putc(' ',fp1);
      /* set position of print head at
         30 column of the paper */

            fprintf(fp1, "%d", p);

            if(p > 1)
                {
            fprintf(fp1, "\n");
            fprintf(fp1, "\n");
                               }

            p++;
              top_of_page=1;
              row=0;
                    }
            }
     }
    if(row<(pl-tm-bm))  /* add blank
                lines at the bottom */
     {
            blank = pl - tm - row - 1;
            for( b=0; b< blank; b++)
                    putc('\n',fp1);

            for(i = 0; i< 30; i++)
            putc(' ',fp1);
      /* set position of print head at
         30 column of the paper */

            fprintf(fp1, "%d", p);
            top_of_page=1;
            row=0;
     }

     p=1;

 }
putc(ESC, fp1);
putc(45, fp1);
putc(0, fp1);
```

(Contd.)

```
        fclose(fp1);
        fclose(fs);
}

/* End of function printer  */

/* Print string function */
/********************************************/
/*              Print italic service        */
/********************************************/
/** THIS IS ROUTINE WHICH WILL PRINTS FILES **/
/********************************************/

/* Function italic_printer */

void italic_printer()
{
        char file[13] ;
        int tm, bm, pl;
        int row=0,i,top_of_page=1,r;
        int p=1;
        int ch,j;
        int number;
        int blank;
        int b;
        FILE *fs, *fp1;
        printf("Enter File: ");
        scanf("%s",file);

        fs=fopen(file,"rb"); /* open source file */

        if(fs==NULL)
        {
                printf("%s",file);
                perror("ERROR : ");
                exit(-1);
        }

        fp1=fopen("/dev/lp0","w"); /* open /dev/lp0
                        system device for print */

        if(fp1==NULL)
```

(Contd.)

```
 {
         printf("%/dev/lp0");
         perror("ERROR : ");
         exit(-1);
 }


printf("NUMBER OF COPY: ");
scanf(" %d",&number);

tm=6;     /* top margin */
bm=8;     /* bottom margin */
pl= 65;  /* page length */

for(j=0;j<number;j++)
 {
         rewind(fs);

 /* Title printing */

         for(i = 0; i< 30; i++)
                 putc(' ',fp1);
             /* set position of print head at
                 30 column of the paper */

         print_string(file); /* print file
                                    name as title */

/************** End ***************/

         while((ch=fgetc(fs)) !=EOF)
          {
                 putc(ESC, fp1);
                 putc(52, fp1);

                 if(top_of_page)
                  {
                      for ( i=0; i<tm; i++)
                         putc('\n',fp1);
                           top_of_page=0;
                  }
                 putc(ch,fp1);
```

(Contd.)

```
                if(ch=='\n')
                {
                    row++;
                   if(row==pl-tm-bm-1)
                       {
                      for(i=0;i<bm;i++)
                          {
                      putc('\n',fp1) ;
                          }

                    for(i = 0; i< 30; i++)
                    putc(' ',fp1);
             /* set position of print head at
                 30 column of the paper */

                    fprintf(fp1, "%d", p);

                        if(p > 1)
                         {
                    fprintf(fp1, "\n");
                    fprintf(fp1, "\n");
                         }

                               p++;
                          top_of_page=1;
                               row=0;
                        }
                }
        }
        if(row<(pl-tm-bm))  /* add blank
                     lines at the bottom */
         {
                blank = pl - tm - row - 1;
                for( b=0; b< blank; b++)
                      putc('\n',fp1);

                for(i = 0; i< 30; i++)
                putc(' ',fp1);
           /* set position of print head at
               30 column of the paper */

                fprintf(fp1, "%d", p);
```

(Contd.)

```
                    top_of_page=1;
                    row=0;
            }

            p=1;

        }
        putc(ESC, fp1);
        putc(53, fp1);
        fclose(fp1);
        fclose(fs);
}

/* End of function printer  */

/* Print string function */
/*******************************************/
/*           Print EMPHSIZED service        */
/*******************************************/
/** THIS IS ROUTINE WHICH WILL PRINTS FILES **/
/*******************************************/

/* Function emphesized_printer */

void emphesized_printer()
{
        char file[13] ;
        int tm, bm, pl;
        int row=0,i,top_of_page=1,r;
        int p=1;
        int ch,j;
        int number;
        int blank;
        int b;
        FILE *fs, *fp1;
        printf("Enter File: ");
        scanf("%s",file);

        fs=fopen(file,"rb"); /* open source file */

        if(fs==NULL)
        {
```

(Contd.)

```
            printf("%s",file);
            perror("ERROR : ");
            exit(-1);
    }

    fp1=fopen("/dev/lp0","w"); /* open /dev/lp0
                        system device for print */

    if(fp1==NULL)
    {
            printf("%/dev/lp0");
            perror("ERROR : ");
            exit(-1);
    }


    printf("NUMBER OF COPY: ");
    scanf(" %d",&number);

    tm=6;      /* top margin */
    bm=8;      /* bottom margin */
    pl=  65;  /* page length */

    for(j=0;j<number;j++)
    {
            rewind(fs);

    /* Title printing */

    for(i = 0; i< 30; i++)
            putc(' ',fp1);
              /* set position of print head at
                 30 column of the paper */

    print_string(file);  /* print file name as
                                      title */

/************** End ***************/

            while((ch=fgetc(fs)) !=EOF)
            {
                    putc(ESC, fp1);
```

(Contd.)

```
          putc(69, fp1);

          if(top_of_page)
           {
        for ( i=0; i<tm; i++)
          putc('\n',fp1);
         top_of_page=0;
           }
          putc(ch,fp1);
          if(ch=='\n')
           {
                 row++;
                if(row==pl-tm-bm-1)
                 {
                for(i=0;i<bm;i++)
                   {
                   putc('\n',fp1) ;
                   }

           for(i = 0; i< 30; i++)
            putc(' ',fp1);
      /* set position of print head at
         30 column of the paper */

          fprintf(fp1, "%d", p);

                  if(p > 1)
                      {
                fprintf(fp1, "\n");
                fprintf(fp1, "\n");
                       }

                         p++;
                    top_of_page=1;
                         row=0;

                 }

           }
     }
    if(row<(pl-tm-bm)) /* add blank
                lines at the bottom */
     {
          blank = pl - tm - row - 1;
```

(Contd.)

```
                        for( b=0; b< blank; b++)
                          putc('\n',fp1);

                        for(i = 0; i< 30; i++)
                          putc(' ',fp1);
                    /* set position of print head at
                       30 column of the paper */
                        fprintf(fp1, "%d", p);
                        top_of_page=1;
                        row=0;
                }

                p=1;

        }
        putc(ESC, fp1);
        putc(70, fp1);
        fclose(fp1);
        fclose(fs);
}

/* End of function printer  */

/* Print string function */

/**********************************************/
/*              Print BOLD service            */
/**********************************************/
/** THIS IS ROUTINE WHICH WILL PRINTS FILES **/
/**********************************************/

/* Function bold_printer */

void bold_printer()
{
        char file[13] ;
        int tm, bm, pl;
        int row=0,i,top_of_page=1,r;
        int p=1;
        int ch,j;
        int number;
        int blank;
```

(Contd.)

```
int b;
FILE *fs, *fp1;
printf("Enter File: ");
scanf("%s",file);

fs=fopen(file,"rb"); /* open source file */

if(fs==NULL)
{
        printf("%s",file);
        perror("ERROR : ");
        exit(-1);
}

fp1=fopen("/dev/lp0","w"); /* open /dev/lp0
                  system device for print */

if(fp1==NULL)
{
        printf("%/dev/lp0");
        perror("ERROR : ");
        exit(-1);
}


printf("NUMBER OF COPY: ");
scanf(" %d",&number);

tm=6;     /* top margin */
bm=8;     /* bottom margin */
pl= 65;  /* page length */

for(j=0;j<number;j++)
{
        rewind(fs);

/* Title printing */

for(i = 0; i< 30; i++)
        putc(' ',fp1);
            /* set position of print head at
              30 column of the paper */
```

(Contd.)

```
print_string(file);   /* print file name as
                         title */

   /************** End ***************/

                  while((ch=fgetc(fs)) !=EOF)
                   {
                          putc(ESC, fp1);
                          putc(71, fp1);

                          if(top_of_page)
                           {
                               for ( i=0; i<tm; i++)
                                     putc('\n',fp1);
                                 top_of_page=0;
                           }
                          putc(ch,fp1);
                          if(ch=='\n')
                           {
                                 row++;
                                if(row==pl-tm-bm-1)
                                 {
                                   for(i=0;i<bm;i++)
                                        {
                                   putc('\n',fp1) ;
                                        }

                       for(i = 0; i< 30; i++)
                        putc(' ',fp1);
                    /* set position of print.head
                       at 30 column of the paper */

                             fprintf(fp1, "%d", p);

                                          if(p > 1)
                                             {
                              fprintf(fp1, "\n");
                             fprintf(fp1, "\n");
                                             }

                                          p++;
                                       top_of_page=1;
```

(Contd.)

```
                                        row=0;
                                }
                        }
                }
                if(row<(pl-tm-bm)) /* add blank
                                lines at the bottom */
                {
                        blank = pl - tm - row - 1;
                        for( b=0; b< blank; b++)
                                putc('\n',fp1);

                        for(i = 0; i< 30; i++)
                                putc(' ',fp1);
                    /* set position of print head at
                        30 column of the paper */
                        fprintf(fp1, "%d", p);
                        top_of_page=1;
                        row=0;
                }

                p=1;

        }
        putc(ESC, fp1);
        putc(72, fp1);
        fclose(fp1);
        fclose(fs);
}

/* End of function printer  */

/* Print string function */
/*******************************************/
/*           Print Elite service          */
/*******************************************/
/** THIS IS ROUTINE WHICH WILL PRINTS FILES **/
/*******************************************/

/* Function elite_printer */

void elite_printer()
{
```

(Contd.)

```
char file[13] ;
int tm, bm, pl;
int row=0,i,top_of_page=1,r;
int p=1;
int ch,j;
int number;
int blank;
int b;
FILE *fs, *fp1;
printf("Enter File: ");
scanf("%s",file);

fs=fopen(file,"rb"); /* open source file */

if(fs==NULL)
{
        printf("%s",file);
        perror("ERROR : ");
        exit(-1);
}

fp1=fopen("/dev/lp0","w"); /* open /dev/lp0
                    system device for print */

if(fp1==NULL)
{
        printf("%/dev/lp0");
        perror("ERROR : ");
        exit(-1);
}


printf("NUMBER OF COPY: ");
scanf(" %d",&number);

tm=6;     /* top margin */
bm=8;     /* bottom margin */
pl= 65;  /* page length */

for(j=0;j<number;j++)
{
        rewind(fs);
```

(Contd.)

```
/* Title printing */

for(i = 0; i< 30; i++)
        putc(' ',fp1);
          /* set position of print head at
             30 column of the paper */

print_string(file);  /* print file name as
                            title */

/************** End ***************/

        while((ch=fgetc(fs)) !=EOF)
         {
                putc(ESC, fp1);
                putc(77, fp1);

                if(top_of_page)
                 {
                    for ( i=0; i<tm; i++)
                           putc('\n',fp1);
                        top_of_page=0;
                 }
                putc(ch,fp1);
                if(ch=='\n')
                 {
                        row++;
                       if(row==pl-tm-bm-1)
                        {
                     for(i=0;i<bm;i++)
                               {
                       putc('\n',fp1) ;
                               }

                for(i = 0; i< 30; i++)
                 putc(' ',fp1);
          /* set position of print head at
             30 column of the paper */
                   fprintf(fp1, "%d", p);

                       if(p > 1)
                             {
```

(Contd.)

```
                                    fprintf(fp1, "\n");
                                    fprintf(fp1, "\n");
                                        }

                                              p++;
                                          top_of_page=1;
                                              row=0;
                                     }

                              }
                       }
                       if(row<(pl-tm-bm)) /* add blank
                                 lines at the bottom */
                       {
                              blank = pl - tm - row - 1;
                              for( b=0; b< blank; b++)
                                    putc('\n',fp1);

                              for(i = 0; i< 30; i++)
                                    putc(' ',fp1);
                         /* set position of print head at
                           30 column of the paper */

                              fprintf(fp1, "%d", p);
                              top_of_page=1;
                              row=0;
                       }

                       p=1;

                 }
                 putc(ESC, fp1);
                 putc(120,fp1);
                 putc(0, fp1);
                 fclose(fp1);
                 fclose(fs);
}

/* End of function printer  */

/* Print string function */
/*******************************************/
/*              Print pica service          */
```

(Contd.)

```
/*********************************************/
/** THIS IS ROUTINE WHICH WILL PRINTS FILES **/
/*********************************************/

/* Function pica_printer */

void pica_printer()
{
        char file[13] ;
        int tm, bm, pl;
        int row=0,i,top_of_page=1,r;
        int p=1;
        int ch,j;
        int number;
        int blank;
        int b;
        FILE *fs, *fp1;
        printf(“Enter File: ”);
        scanf(“%s”,file);

        fs=fopen(file,”rb”); /* open source file */

        if(fs==NULL)
        {
                printf(“%s”,file);
                perror(“ERROR : ”);
                exit(-1);
        }

        fp1=fopen(“/dev/lp0”,”w”); /* open /dev/lp0
                                system device for print */

        if(fp1==NULL)
        {
                printf(“%/dev/lp0”);
                perror(“ERROR : ”);
                exit(-1);
        }


        printf(“NUMBER OF COPY: ”);
        scanf(“ %d”,&number);
```

(Contd.)

```
    tm=6;      /* top margin */
    bm=8;      /* bottom margin */

    pl= 65; /* page length */

    for(j=0;j<number;j++)
     {
            rewind(fs);

    /* Title printing */

    for(i = 0; i< 30; i++)
            putc(' ',fp1);
              /* set position of print head at
                 30 column of the paper */

    print_string(file);  /* print file name as
                            title */

/************** End ***************/

            while((ch=fgetc(fs)) !=EOF)
             {
                   putc(ESC, fp1);
                   putc(80, fp1);

                   if(top_of_page)
                    {
                        for ( i=0; i<tm; i++)
                               putc('\n',fp1);
                          top_of_page=0;
                    }
                   putc(ch,fp1);
                   if(ch=='\n')
                    {
                          row++;
                         if(row==pl-tm-bm-1)
                          {
                            for(i=0;i<bm;i++)
                                {
                             putc('\n',fp1) ;
                                }
```

(Contd.)

```
            for(i = 0; i< 30; i++)
             putc(' ',fp1);
        /* set position of print head at
            30 column of the paper */
               fprintf(fp1, "%d", p);

                           if(p > 1)
                            {
               fprintf(fp1, "\n");
              fprintf(fp1, "\n");
                            }

                           p++;
                        top_of_page=1;
                           row=0;
                  }
          }
   }
  if(row<(pl-tm-bm)) /* add blank
            lines at the bottom */
   {
         blank = pl - tm - row - 1;
         for( b=0; b< blank; b++)
              putc('\n',fp1);

         for(i = 0; i< 30; i++)
              putc(' ',fp1);
      /* set position of print head at
          30 column of the paper */

         fprintf(fp1, "%d", p);
         top_of_page=1;
         row=0;
   }

  p=1;

}
putc(ESC, fp1);
putc(120,fp1);
putc(0,fp1);
fclose(fp1);
```

(Contd.)

```
        fclose(fs);
}

/* End of function printer  */

/* Print string function */
/*********************************************/
/*            Print default service           */
/*********************************************/
/** THIS IS ROUTINE WHICH WILL PRINTS FILES **/
/*********************************************/

/* Function default_printer */

void def_mode_printer(void)
{
        char file[13] ;
        int tm, bm, pl;
        int row=0,i,top_of_page=1,r;
        int p=1;
        int ch,j;
        int number;
        int blank;
        int b;
        FILE *fs, *fp1;
        printf("Enter File: ");
        scanf("%s",file);

        fs=fopen(file,"rb"); /* open source file */

        if(fs==NULL)
        {
                printf("%s",file);
                perror("ERROR : ");
                exit(-1);
        }

        fp1=fopen("/dev/lp0","w"); /* open /dev/lp0
                          system device for print */

        if(fp1==NULL)
        {
```

(Contd.)

```
            printf("%/dev/lp0");
            perror("ERROR : ");
            exit(-1);
    }

    printf("NUMBER OF COPY: ");
    scanf(" %d",&number);

    tm=6;     /* top margin */
    bm=8;     /* bottom margin */
    pl= 65;  /* page length */

    for(j=0;j<number;j++)
    {
            rewind(fs);

    /* Title printing */

    for(i = 0; i< 30; i++)
            putc(' ',fp1);
                /* set position of print head at
                   30 column of the paper */

    print_string(file); /* print file name as
                           title */

/**************** End ****************/

            while((ch=fgetc(fs)) !=EOF)
            {
                    putc(ESC, fp1);
                    putc(120, fp1);
                    putc(0, fp1);
                    if(top_of_page)
                    {
                        for ( i=0; i<tm; i++)
                                putc('\n',fp1);
                            top_of_page=0;
                    }
                    putc(ch,fp1);
                    if(ch=='\n')
                    {
```

(Contd.)

```
row++;
if(row==pl-tm-bm-1)
    {
        for(i=0;i<bm;i++)
            {
         putc('\n',fp1) ;
            }

        for(i = 0; i< 30; i++)
            putc(' ',fp1);
 /* set position of print head at
     30 column of the paper */

     fprintf(fp1, "%d", p);

                if(p > 1)
                    {
      fprintf(fp1, "\n");
     fprintf(fp1, "\n");
                    }
                p++;
             top_of_page=1;
                row=0;

            }
    }

}
if(row<(pl-tm-bm))  /* add blank
            lines at the bottom */
{
    blank = pl - tm - row - 1;
    for( b=0; b< blank; b++)
            putc('\n',fp1);

    for(i = 0; i< 30; i++)
            putc(' ',fp1);
  /* set position of print head at
      30 column of the paper */

    fprintf(fp1, "%d", p);
    top_of_page=1;
    row=0;
}
```

(Contd.)

```
            p=1;

         }
        fclose(fp1);
        fclose(fs);
}

/* End of function printer  */

/* Print string function */

/******************************************/
/*          Print near letter service     */
/******************************************/
/** THIS IS ROUTINE WHICH WILL PRINTS FILES **/
/******************************************/

/* Function near_printer */

void near_printer()
{
        char file[13] ;
        int tm, bm, pl;
        int row=0,i,top_of_page=1,r;
        int p=1;
        int ch,j;
        int number;
        int blank;
        int b;
        FILE *fs, *fp1;
        printf("Enter File: ");
        scanf("%s",file);

        fs=fopen(file,"rb"); /* open source file */

        if(fs==NULL)
        {
                printf("%s",file);
                perror("ERROR : ");
                exit(-1);
        }
```

(Contd.)

```
fp1=fopen("/dev/lp0","w"); /* open /dev/lp0
                  system device for print */

if(fp1==NULL)
{
        printf("%/dev/lp0");
        perror("ERROR : ");
        exit(-1);
}

printf("NUMBER OF COPY: ");
scanf(" %d",&number);

tm=6;      /* top margin */
bm=8;      /* bottom margin */
pl= 65;  /* page length */

for(j=0;j<number;j++)
{
        rewind(fs);

/* Title printing */

for(i = 0; i< 30; i++)
        putc(' ',fp1);
          /* set position of print head at
             30 column of the paper */

print_string(file);  /* print file name as
                             title */

/*************** End ***************/

        while((ch=fgetc(fs)) !=EOF)
        {
                putc(ESC, fp1);
                putc(120, fp1);
                putc(1,fp1);
                if(top_of_page)
                {
                    for ( i=0; i<tm; i++)
                            putc('\n',fp1);
```

(Contd.)

```
                top_of_page=0;
        }
        putc(ch,fp1);
        if(ch=='\n')
        {
                row++;
                if(row==pl-tm-bm-1)
                {
            for(i=0;i<bm;i++)
                        {
            putc('\n',fp1) ;
                        }

            for(i = 0; i< 30; i++)
              putc(' ',fp1);
   /* set position of print head at
      30 column of the paper */
            fprintf(fp1, "%d", p);

                        if(p > 1)
                           {
           fprintf(fp1, "\n");
           fprintf(fp1, "\n");
                           }

                        p++;
                    top_of_page=1;
                        row=0;
                }
        }
}
if(row<(pl-tm-bm))  /* add blank
              lines at the bottom */
{
        blank = pl - tm - row - 1;
        for( b=0; b< blank; b++)
                putc('\n',fp1);

        for(i = 0; i< 30; i++)
                putc(' ',fp1);
  /* set position of print head at
     30 column of the paper */
```

(Contd.)

```
                              fprintf(fp1, "%d", p);
                               top_of_page=1;
                               row=0;
                        }

                        p=1;

                }
                putc(ESC, fp1);
                putc(120, fp1);
                putc(0, fp1);
                fclose(fp1);
                fclose(fs);
}

/* End of function printer  */

/* Print string function */

/*********************************************/
/* Print spacing 1/8 default is 1/16 service */
/*********************************************/
/** THIS IS ROUTINE WHICH WILL PRINTS FILES **/
/*********************************************/

void spacing_printer()
{
        char file[13] ;
        int tm, bm, pl;
        int row=0,i,top_of_page=1,r;
        int p=1;
        int ch,j;
        int number;
        int blank;
        int b;
        FILE *fs, *fp1;
        printf("Enter File: ");
        scanf("%s",file);

        fs=fopen(file,"rb"); /* open source file */

        if(fs==NULL)
```

(Contd.)